SHOWING LIVESTOCK
Edward Hart

DAVID & CHARLES
Newton Abbot London North Pomfret (Vt)

DEDICATED to all stock men and women who rise early
and go to bed late so that their charges at the big shows may
approach perfection

British Library Cataloguing in Publication Data

Hart, Edward
    Showing livestock.
    1. Livestock exhibitions
    I. Title
    636.08'88   SF114

    ISBN 0–7153–7537–7

Library of Congress Catalog Card Number 78–74086

Set by Northern Phototypesetting Company, Bolton, Greater Manchester
and printed in Great Britain
by Redwood Burn Limited, Trowbridge and Esher
for David & Charles (Publishers) Limited
Brunel House Newton Abbot Devon

Published in the United States of America
by David & Charles Inc
North Pomfret Vermont 05053 USA

Contents

Acknowledgements

Without the specialist and professional help of breeders of Britain's many classes of livestock this book would not have been possible. Those who gave freely of their time and skill include:

Dick Adams; American Polled Hereford Association; Arthur Bell; Jean Brown; Jack Bulmer; Dairy Shorthorn Society; John Davy; Ray Dent; Tom Fulton; Hereford Cattle Society; Robin Hope; Max Jones; Donald McLean; Bert Manning; National Federation of Young Farmers' Clubs; National Pig Breeders' Association; Jean Ritchie; Jill Salmon; Paul Sapsed; Robert Trow-Smith; Ron Turner; Robert Vigus; Elizabeth West; and Audrey Wickham who compiled the index.

1 The Show Scene

The world's agricultural shows attract hundreds of thousands of visitors and are the scene of millions of pounds' worth of business annually. They may be staged on a vast permanent site employing a large staff of professional organisers, or in a village field. In either event they are a focal point for an important section of the community.

The farm show is as important to the machinery dealer, the feed compounder and the fertiliser manufacturer as to the stockbreeder. It is the shop window *par excellence* for all of them. Successful livestock breeders have often been great salesmen and wonderful show men.

What are shows for?

Not everyone in all the agricultural community approves of showing. Many connected with the land pass through a stage—I did myself—where economic considerations seem all-important, and when things not directly connected with earning a living from one's farming activities are irrelevant. This is to ignore the stimulus of well turned-out stock to those who have no intention of competing but who return to their cattle, sheep or pigs after a day at a show determined to keep them a little cleaner, feed them a little better, handle them a trifle more quietly.

Other industries coined the phrase 'job satisfaction'; farming has no need for it. Work and pleasure are inextricably rolled into one in so many farming activities, especially on the livestock side. The big shows engender a unique comradeship among competititors, who meet not only in the show-ring but in the evenings before and after the big occasion, and in no profession is help more readily given to the young competitor and potential rival.

Show societies played an invaluable part in establishing

Britain as 'the stud farm of the world'. They followed the
famous sheep-shearings of the Duke of Bedford at Woburn,
Bedfordshire, and of Coke at Holkham in Norfolk in 1777. Sir
John Sinclair spoke at the dinner held on the occasion of the
first 'Highland' show at Edinburgh in 1822, in words that have
not been bettered in the succeeding century and a half:

> Such meetings excite a spirit of improvement. Much
> advantage is derived from the discussions which they
> occasion and from the opportunities they afford of viewing
> the various descriptions of live stock which the country
> possesses and comparing their respective properties and
> defects.

Our shows have progressed steadily from competitions for
individual conformation to production/conformation classes
in the dairying world, liveweight gain/conformation in beef,
and various forms of progeny class. If the dairy bull's sole
purpose is to produce high-yielding daughters giving
satisfactory milk, the fact remains that he is sure to be a prime
object of inspection by any farming visitor. As West Riding
Ayrshire breeder, the late Edgar Greenwood, said: 'You've got
to live with him. So choose a good looker!' Pride in stock is the
first step to improvement. Dedication to the job in hand is an
unfashionable virtue, but is a necessary one where livestock
and show-ring successes are sought.

Showing sets breed standards. Were it not for shows, every
breeder would have his or her own ideas of perfection, and the
result would be fragmentation and a wide range of type and
colour. Many a breeder has lived with his stock for so long and
so closely that he has become firmly convinced that they are
perfect, that there is no higher goal at which to aim. Only when
they stand alongside others in the show-ring do their
imperfections appear, and that realisation is the root of
improvement. All exhibitors must aspire to the highest
standards, or sell their stock for less money.

Reasons for showing livestock range from a wish to help the
local village event to a determination to establish a name at

national or international level. In the end the will to win really counts. This book contains much knowledge freely given by top-class stockmen and women, but without the drive, attention to detail and unremitting effort associated with the very highest level of livestock husbandry, knowledge alone will not prevail.

One leading pig exhibitor walked his pigs religiously twice a day during the season; even after church on Sunday evenings he changed his clothes and walked his pigs. Others stress the vital importance of regular routine. Feeding to the minute on a 'little and often' basis entails giving up many ordinary pleasures and relaxations. In particular, the late evening feed is highly regarded by a wide range of stockmen.

The stockman's eye

A number of features are common to all classes of stock. 'Start with the animal' has been stressed by cattle, pig and sheep exhibitors alike.

A fairly recent innovation is the Duke of Edinburgh's Trophy competition for stockmen, staged at the Royal Show. All competitors must place in order of merit either a ring of four beef animals, a ring of four dairy animals, a ring of four fat lambs or a ring of four breeding pigs. The competitors indicate their choice on the entry form. They then estimate the liveweight of a pig and a lamb, and take part in an identification competition. A livestock husbandry and veterinary quiz follows, each correct answer gaining ten points. Ten minutes are allowed for each section of the competition. The method of awarding points is based on Young Farmers' Club national rules, but reasons for the placings are not required.

To qualify, a competitor must be employed by one of the cattle, sheep or pig exhibitors at that particular Royal Show, and must personally have fed or supervised the feeding of the animals at the show. The contest emphasises the importance of 'the stockman's eye' which comes only through experience and observation and which must be developed by every potential show man.

This book has been made possible only through the unstinted help of leading exhibitors, who have brought out points often neglected or taken for granted. Throughout these pages the term 'stockman' or 'herdsman' implies 'stockman or stockwoman', 'herdsman or herdswoman' — the term 'stockperson' is distinctly uninspiring. Men and women are included equally in every facet of the meticulous, fascinating, skilled yet sometimes tedious business of preparing stock for show and sale.

2   On the Day

A British country showground is unique—it has an atmosphere compounded of stock, people and rural surroundings. Exhibitors in white smocks and judges and stewards in formal hats contrast with the ceaseless call of side-show attendants and the colourful throng of the spectators.

There is nowhere like a show for meeting friends. Walk among the crowds at any rural show, and you are certain to chance on a pair of cronies meeting for the first time in a twelvemonth or in twenty years. The gaiety of these greetings per-colates through the ground, adding to the general uplift of spirits.

But no show is complete without livestock. This was proved, sadly but beyond doubt, during the disastrous foot-and-mouth disease epidemic which began in 1967. Smithfield without stock was not Smithfield, even though the greater part of the Earls Court exhibition is given over to machinery.

Of course, the perfect show is held under blue skies. Cold and wet weather dampens the spirits of the most ardent show-goer. A succession of wet show days is enough to bankrupt a small society, and has done so on several occasions. Such days are best forgotten. In the show of memory and hope the sun is always shining, though not too strongly, for a really sweltering day on a large showground like the Royal becomes very tiring. Sun, a light breeze and ample shade for stock and spectators make the most enjoyable combination.

Quite the best parts of show day come before and after the general opening. This does not exclude the non-exhibitor, for an interested spectator is seldom told to leave after the gates have officially closed. Evening is the time for 'all the fun of the fair', and it starts on the evening before the show with the arrival of waggons of livestock ready for judging the next day.

The heavy vehicles roll to a halt within range of the stock's quarters. Grooms, herdsmen, shepherds or pigmen jump out, lower the creaking ramps, open the slatted doors and take a reassuring glance inside. Receiving directions from the steward, they proceed to unload the animals under their care into the appropriate stalls or boxes.

This is seldom achieved without incident. The waggon which the Guernsey bull entered so unwillingly in his own yard has become a safe haven. He has no intention of leaving it. Only concerted efforts combined with tact and bribery result in his finally slithering and stumbling down the ramp to be led off to his temporary home.

Pigs are not the easiest of creatures to direct, and the relief of being free from a jolting trailer may go to the porcine head and result in undesirable frolics before the allotted pen is reached. Everywhere there is passage of animals; a Shire strides steadfastly behind a slip of a girl on the end of a halter shank; a diminutive grey Welsh pony stallion threatens to drag three men with him; a Hereford bull walks as placidly as though at exercise on the farm.

At the big shows this process goes on throughout the night. Summer dusk falls, but the thoughts of an early start do not stand between a dedicated exhibitor and a night's enjoyment—for many this is the year's holiday. Their stock comes first, but once the animals are seen to and sheeted down for the night there is a great chance to catch up on breed news.

If judging is on the following day, a very early start is essential. Stock must be fed, groomed and watered; no detail is omitted that might jeopardise the efforts of the past months. There is a magic in this hour at the big shows; the Royal Highland with its tall trees; the Royal Welsh as the mist lifts on the overlooking hills; the leafy English Royal in the heart of fertile Warwickshire.

The men and women cleaning and walking their stock in the early morning are competitors. Before nightfall some will have won and the rest be disappointed. Yet all belong to the brotherhood of stockmen, and none will refuse to help a rival who may inadvertently have left behind some necessary piece of equipment. Above all they are professionals. They spend their working lives among stock, earn their livings through their charges, speak a common language. Though the stockman's interest is partly mercenary, this identification with a chosen career marks him out from many other professions.

Some of the world's best stock are met on these early morning jaunts; a line of brown-and-white Ayrshires wending their way to the milking area, Welsh pigs snuffling at exercise, Blackface or Cheviot sheep receiving their final manicures. In the changing rooms rows of hard-bitten stockmen, joking as they shave, comment (usually justifiably) on the spartan facilities or compare the Three Counties with the Bath and West.

Main-ring display teams are also up and about at this hour. Recently, I chanced to breakfast with the Royal Canadian Mounties, and over bacon and eggs listened to yarns of the breeding of their famous blacks. These splendid horses came alive as their foibles were discussed in detail, their training methods described. But for the Royal Highland, such things would have remained remote for life. And so it is for the many whose lives have been enriched through the pressure, competition and glamour of the show-ring.

From around nine o'clock the crowds pour in, each person adding to the excitement. The main-ring stands fill, stalls do brisk business and smart-suited machinery attendants beguile customers with brightly painted ironwork. There is interest in the main ring for a full day's viewing and, equally, plenty to see without once sitting down in that central arena. As the day wears on, the Grand Parade of winning animals circles in front of the Royal Box, each breed described by a competent commentator until the long, snaking line finally leaves, and the ring is cleared for jumping, sheepdog handling or Young Farmers' Club classes.

The sun descends over the mosaic of hues, car parks begin to empty and hubbub gives way to stillness. The horses, cattle and sheep have been fed for the evening, the goats milked, the pigs grunt contentedly. With the judging behind them, tension for the exhibitors slackens. The hour before dusk becomes one of the best in show, as people relax with time for talk.

On a pile of bales sit a group of Scottish stockmen. That they chat near the lines of Ayrshire cattle is by no means conclusive proof of their country of origin, for Ayrshires are found

throughout Britain. Their Scottish tongue and the profes-
sionalism of their talk show how much the long lives and
high yields of their charges mean to them. Across the alley
another Scot flips a few handfuls of straw round a gleaming
black Angus bull, the red rosette pinned proudly above his
head indicating his supremacy.

From the row of loose boxes opposite comes a systematic
thump-thump-thump as a Percheron stallion tries conclusions
with the woodwork of his box. His groom calls to him to desist,
and round comes the great grey head as the horse peers over
his half-door at the sound of the familiar, respected voice. We
talk of French Percherons, Canadian Percherons, of the value
of this clean-legged breed on city streets and on farms. The
brewery teams of Shires are now snug behind green sheets
which guard them from disturbance, but here and there the
fine, clean head of a well-bred hunter pokes into the cool
evening air, placid eye unchanging as its neck is patted by a
passing hand.

Needs of stock and exhibitors

In one respect all competitors can add to the smooth running of
a show. Neatness and orderliness have an impact on the
viewing public, encouraging them to keep the showground
clean too. If pens are left with straw, manure and gear strewn
haphazardly about, similar untidy behaviour may be expected
from spectators.

At some shows a prize is awarded for the neatest stall. This
admirable idea should be followed more widely, and is usually
carried out by an inspecting judge without warning of any
precise time. Tools together, bedding neat, manure tidily
awaiting collection, freedom from loose straw, are all factors
sought by the inspectors' keen eyes. One lady lost points
through having the canvas protecting her Clun Forest sheep
from draught on the outside instead of the inside of the hurdle.
Bare hurdles are a temptation as rubbing posts.

Clean water is another essential. The judge will look askance
at water that has obviously been in front of the animal for some

time. The biggest problem in keeping show quarters in order is the too-friendly attitude of non-stock people who poke fingers into a carefully carded fleece or rub their hands made oily from a ram's head on to its clean wool.

The pens may be far from perfect so a few joiner's tools, nails and screws are an essential part of the show man's kit. Horses in particular are liable to tear at any loose fittings, preferring old tarpaulin to new hay. Show animals must have rest, and at a multi-day show the tarpaulins are set in place early in the evening to ensure peace and privacy for the stock, rather than as essential covering to keep out the cold.

Although animal needs vary, attendants must pack roughly the same items for their own use whether they deal with horses, cattle, sheep, pigs or goats. A list well worth drawing up for the novice includes chairs, a table, beds and bedding. For cooking and heating water, bottled gas is preferable to paraffin as there is less smell and, vitally important, less fire risk.

Crockery and sufficient food for the stay must be added; showground food stalls tend to be very expensive. A washing-up bowl and detergent are needed, as well as a kettle and pans. Wellington boots are a 'must', and sufficient changes of clothing to last the trip, including a change for the evenings.

Showgrounds vary considerably in the accommodation offered to stockmen. A cabin of barest boards is available at some centres, providing space to erect a bed or lay out a sleeping blanket, but nothing else. There may be washing facilities, but things like mirrors tend to be in short supply. Though times have changed since stockmen were expected to sleep in the hay or the waggon, there is scope for very considerable improvement at the majority of shows where the stock people are the basis of the whole entertainment.

Owner-exhibitors form a larger proportion than most show organisers recognise. Having furnished their own homes comfortably, they are taken aback by the primitiveness of showground accommodation. And employed stockmen have just as much right to comfort. They put their stock first in all circumstances, rise early and go to bed late, and should be given more consideration than they at present receive.

3   Cattle—General

To show cattle successfully you must love them. It's no good just liking them. The show-ring has been criticised on the grounds that exhibitors do not go for commercial points. This is untrue.

To win in the ring a cow must walk well, and to give high yields she must be able to walk to and from her pasture without difficulty, and move freely about her grazing area. Show men like a neat, even udder with level sole and well-placed teats. By breeding for milk only, it would be quite easy to finish up with a huge pendulous udder that attracted damage, and teats sticking outwards from the perpendicular—north, south, east and west, in cattlemen's terminology. Teats at this angle are unsuitable for milking machines, as the weight of the teat cups pulls the teats down and cuts off the milk supply. Then follow all sorts of troubles and lowered yields. Because exhibitors are particular about their cows' teat placings, the trait is improved right through the dairy industry.

A farmer may show cows from his pedigree herd, but he still milks those cows and sells their milk every day of the year. The critics of showing tend to live off what show people have found out, and done.

Without doubt, it is more difficult to show dairy animals than beef. The beef animal is prepared before the show and, provided it has been taught to lead and handle quietly, there is not so much to go wrong as with a milk cow whose yield may be upset by the strange surroundings.

Leading

All show stock must be trained to the halter. This remark might seem too obvious were it not for the painful exhibitions that occur from time to time when a heifer has patently been insufficiently accustomed to being led.

There are various methods of training. Undoubtedly the best time is with the young calf, when the human is much stronger than the animal, and the lesson then taught remains for life. Teaching calves to lead is an admirable job for sensible children, benefiting both parties, but in today's large herds this counsel of perfection may be impractical. Modern aids enable the herdsman to tend more stock; they don't really make life easier or more leisurely.

When a large number of young calves are born yearly, we must accept that all will not be taught to lead. The method of training the adult varies. Some prefer the gradual approach, simply placing the halter round the animal's neck, and taking a month over the process of learning. The more abrupt method adopted by other competent herdsmen is to fit on the halter securely, tie the beast to a nearby wall and leave it to do battle with the immovable object. At the end of twenty-four hours, the necessary subservience is claimed. Having learned to respect the halter, the animal is then handled gently and taught to lead by regular daily outings.

When walking a led animal, the handler holds the halter shank in his right hand, fairly close to the animal's head. He takes the slack of the shank in his left hand, but never wraps the rope tightly round his hand. Neglect of this simple rule has led to nasty accidents. Stock are invariably led on the handler's offside, and usually circle the ring in a clockwise direction, but this must be checked at each show. Thus the animal is between judge and handler, and the latter does not obscure the judge's view at any time.

When leading stock, especially young or unruly animals, take care over clothes and footwear. I was once exercising a year-old Ayrshire bull with straight, short horns. He was of stubborn rather than nasty disposition, but he hooked one horn under a strong leather belt which I was wearing too slackly, and took me running backwards towards the corner of a stone barn only avoided at the last second. Moral: don't wear slack or floppy clothing on exercise.

Wellington boots on a tarmac surface offer little grip. Nailed boots and a stoned road are the best combination: if footwear is too light, even quite a young heifer can make herself felt if she inadvertently steps on the foot while turning. Keeping the right arm rigid when making a left-hand turn helps this manoeuvre. Special techniques for dealing with bulls are considered later (see p. 41).

Dairy and beef points

It is probably more difficult to get a perfect dairy female than a bull. The udder is the all-important feature and there is so much at risk with it, as all cattlemen know. The task of calving down at a fairly precise date is no mean one, but the female temperament is usually easier to deal with, especially in the Jersey breed where well-managed cows are a delight to handle and the bulls tend to be nasty.

In male or female, beef or dairy, correctness of leg is one of the first things a judge seeks. We see two distinct faults here. Hind legs may be bred too straight, causing a stiff, swinging motion as the animal walks. Continental imports have a tendency in this direction and, as it is less familiar in British strains, it is a point to be watched.

The reverse is the sickle hock that goes too far underneath. It is especially prevalent in milk cows with heavy udders. The beast then walks with a paddling, circular motion, not placing one foot in front of the other, and is liable to go lame through using feet and joints at wrong angles.

'A leg at each corner' is a hackneyed phrase for all manner of stock. It indicates well set-out legs which stand upright; the wrong ones are too close in front, almost brushing each other in passing, or spread-eagled.

The topline is as straight as possible in most breeds, especially beef. 'A block of meat on four short legs' is a description of the Angus, whose legs are not bred as short as they were. A long, curving sweep of back is sought in males of breeds like the Simmental.

Cattlemen have always liked an animal with a good topline. That great provoker of original thought, the late Professor 'Bobby' Boutflour, demanded: 'You say you like a cow with a

An excellent study in handling methods at the Royal Show. The boar on the right is being tempted by a titbit in the stockman's hand; the foreground pig walks guided only by the flat show stick, while one to the left of centre is being steadied by use of the board. Many hours of work have combined to bring adult boars to this degree of quietness *(National Pig Breeders' Association)*

Large White sows at the Royal: note the speckless condition of this fine entry, and their accessibility to the judge. Pigs that cannot be approached stand small hope of tickets. Though pigs may be cleaned they cannot be trimmed like cattle and sheep, so the exhibitor depends more on condition brought out by correct feeding *(National Pig Breeders' Association)*

(above) Early morning at the Great Yorkshire Show: exercise is a vital part of preparation, and this British Saddleback sow responds well to her young handler. Note the row of evenly spaced teats; fourteen is the optimum number

(right) Method of leading a stud bull: a chain is clipped on to his ring, while another passes below his chin from the off to the near side of his leather head-collar. All stock are led from the near side, that is, on the handler's right, and usually go round the ring in a clockwise direction keeping the animal between judge and handler

(below) Channel Island cattle on parade: the animal approaching is being helped to keep her head up; no stock walk well with their heads down. Jerseys are a delight to show and handle if properly reared

straight back. I ask you why. You say, "To give it strength". What do you want strength in its back for? Are you going to ride the damned thing to hounds?' Against this, veterinary surgeon R H Smythe, MRCVS, wrote in *The Anatomy of Dog Breeding*: 'If ever man succeeds in producing an animal possessing a perfect spine, he will have gone very far towards producing the perfect animal.' This connection between head, trunk and limbs is vital, and Smythe's views the more nearly coincide with those of breeders of many generations of farm stock. Wearability is a very positive economic factor, associated with sound legs, feet and topline.

Similarly, stockmen from every country with whom I have talked are adamant in seeking a 'good head'. On the hook, the head is the lowest priced part; on the live animal it indicates the whole character. A dairy head differs from a beef head in being longer, but a broad muzzle is liked in all classes. The wider the cutting area of the mouth, the higher the rate of consumption.

The neck should blend neatly into the shoulder. A certain show animal was criticised for being 'in three pieces'. This is a descriptive phrase to the cattleman—its head was all right, its quarters sound, but the shoulders did not blend with either the neck or the barrel. It did not appear as a smooth, single entity.

There was a move to breed dairy cows very round in the barrel, but not all modern judges favour this. They prefer *depth* of barrel, in any breed. This is an outstanding factor in a really high-class Ayrshire herd—and there are many—compared with a second-rate one.

Flat, rather than round, bone is sought in all cattle. One judge's comment on the milk vessel is that a very deep hind udder is needed—so deep that one can't tell where it starts and finishes, reaching right up to the tail.

The milk vein is vital on a dairy cow. It should be thick and knotted, ending well along the belly in wide milk wells. A cow with a lot of vein on the udder surface almost always milks well. I recall a cow in a well-known northern Friesian herd which was being judged by our Young Farmers' Club. 'A good-looking nothing' was the farmer's description of that cow. She had everything—conformation, fine skin, neat udder—except

large milk veins. They were only of finger thickness, and the
cow was a poor milker despite her other attributes.

'A tail like a whiplash and an udder that will go in your
waistcoat pocket when milked out' are other traditional but still
very apt descriptions of dairy characteristics.

Selling store cattle

Though store cattle may pass over a weighbridge en route for
the auction ring, the vendor's job is still to catch the buyer's
eye. That gentleman is concerned not only with the price per
hundredweight he is paying at the sale, but with growth
potential. A smart-looking animal that has obviously had some
care and attention is the more likely to carry on growing at the
desired rate.

Dealers buy hundreds of thousands of cattle each year. They
must resell, probably immediately. They are more likely to be
thought well of by their customers if they present an even batch
of cared-for cattle, even when commission and transport have
raised the bill. The vendor of store cattle must cater for such
needs.

The first essential is to select an even batch. Never put roans
and blacks together; colour is more than skin-deep in cattle
breeding, and may indicate different breeding and therefore
different reaction to feed and environment. The cattle feeder
requires bunches that grow together and go to market together,
so that he can bring in another lot in one clean sweep. Make his
job easy by offering level lots—better a bunch of bad ones than
good and bad all mixed up.

All yard-fed beasts must be dehorned. Most are, but some
are done so carelessly that the remaining horn needs attention
under local anaesthetic in the adult animal. A part-grown,
malformed horn entirely spoils the look of a beast, so
dehorning at calf stage is a job calling for care, not one to be
rushed or delegated to a beginner.

Matching for size and colour is, of course, more simple in the
bigger herds. A smaller grazier has to take extra care that stock
he rears and buys will match fairly well when selling day

comes. A level, thriving lot of cattle makes the inevitable weekend routine easier to bear than tending nondescripts.

Sex is specially important when making up pens. Bullocks in one, heifers in another is an obvious but sometimes neglected choice. Bullocks and heifers of the same breed have different growth rates, and bulling heifers among a yard of bullocks are a great nuisance, causing loss of energy and therefore poorer feed conversion through constant riding.

Some time before sale, store cattle should be put through the crush and generally tidied up. Clipping along the spine, cleaning heads, flanks and tails improves appearances out of all proportion to the few minutes taken per beast. The biggest mistake is to leave the job till the day before the sale, as stock will be upset and look hollow through being kept from food while waiting their turn.

Stock keep cleanest at grass; but grass, especially spring grass, can cause scouring which results in the cattle mucking themselves up while in the transport, and coming out at the far end in a fearful state. Sweet hay or clean straw should be offered in the field for a couple of days before the sale, and is eaten surprisingly well even on lush and ample grazing. This coarse fodder stiffens the dung, besides helping to make cattle look and feel contented.

Waggon size should be estimated accurately. This is difficult in practice, for choice is seldom available and it is tempting to push all the beasts in to clear a yard. Yet several experts have told me that they have lost money through putting just one too many into a transport, to find them emerging sweating and filthy at the market.

Quiet handling is essential. The cattle are going to strange surroundings where the drovers' patience is tried by the pressure of numbers. One's own stock can at least be given a good start with care and patience when loading. In this respect proper handling crushes and loading pens are a boon; most of us have memories of chasing cattle several times round a field before finally cornering them near the field gate and forcing them reluctantly up a chute consisting of old gates tied together with binder twine. Modern designs of handling facilities need only be installed once, and save not only time and temper but a very considerable amount of condition on stock.

The store sale is the culmination of months of management that should include routine control of scurf and lice. Ringworm and warbles both affect the appearance of cattle and both are controllable, though ringworm has a distressing habit of appearing even among well fed stock and is one of the few cattle complaints transferable to humans.

4   Cattle—Beef

The purpose of any meat animal is to convert vegetable and waste material into human food. Not only do we seek quantity of meat, but texture and flavour, two factors that make the meat pleasant to eat. Each meat animal carries only a certain proportion of eatable flesh which is called its 'killing-out percentage'. The aim of feeder, exhibitor and judge is an animal with a high killing-out percentage coupled with texture and flavour. These are properly determined only after the animal is dead, but judging on the hoof, as live judging is called, draws on the experience gained in the past by noting slaughterhouse results, and applying it to the stock in question. Average killing-out figures are: cattle, 60 per cent, sheep, 55 per cent, pigs, 73 per cent.

Meat production is a business like any other, in which highest returns compatible with inputs are sought. Certain parts of an animal produce better quality, and therefore more expensive, joints than others, and so the breeder's and feeder's aim is an animal well developed and thickly fleshed in those better parts. In cattle these lie *above* an imaginary line drawn from the animal's hock to the point of its shoulder.

Beef points

The top and underlines must be straight and nearly parallel to each other, and the body as a whole must look *balanced*. If in your mind's eye you divide the animal into three parts these, though not equal, should seem to balance each other. The three parts are: poll to behind the shoulders; shoulders to hook bones; hook bones to tail head.

The beef animal must be deep, and stand on straight, moderately short legs set at the four 'corners'. The general appearance is low-set.

'Good bone' is a stockman's term easier to say than to

define. Though bone is not needed in the butcher's shop, each animal must have sufficient to carry its carcass. It should be there when viewed from both directions above the hock. Sound bone without coarseness indicates constitution.

The back must be moderately long and of even width. The beef animal's back is quite different from that of a dairy heifer, which is wedge-shaped. Width at the loins and tail head is needed. Well-sprung ribs contrast with a flat-sided animal; champions invariably have a certain spring of rib associated with heart room and constitution. Long, wide and well-fleshed hindquarters are essential for they carry the expensive cuts of meat. A deep and full flank, fleshed right down to the hocks, often distinguishes the first-rate from the second-rate animal, while hip bones should be covered and not prominent.

Viewed from behind, the animal must be full between the legs, which are set wide apart giving square and full hindquarters. From the front, the beast should 'meet' you well, with wide full chest, and wide but not rough or prominent shoulders which are level and full on top. Skin should be supple when handled and the hair fine and silky. A thick, tight and hard hide indicates slow maturity and poor killing-out percentage, though a hide may be so thin as to indicate lack of hardiness.

Flesh should be firm, smooth and mellow, especially over the shoulders, ribs, loin and rump. Patchiness or unevenness is a sign of poor quality fleshing and waste fat. It is most often found on the hindquarters.

Breeding stock

The points discussed so far are directly concerned with the butcher's needs, and therefore those of the judge of fat cattle. Butchers' animals must be bred in the first place, and judging them is not quite the same as judging stock to carry on the line. When judging breeding cattle, the most important point for males is conformation. This must be of breed type. A beef-breeding animal for the lowlands, for example, the Angus, is black and polled, as is the Galloway which lives on the hills.

The Galloway's conformation is not so 'beefy', yet it is ideally suited to its environment. In addition to points already considered, the beef bull for breeding must have a strong, wide and clean-cut head, with large, prominent, alert eyes and a covering of good quality hair. Head and neck should be well up on the shoulders and not appear to be coming out of the chest. A well developed crest adds to the general appearance of burly, masculine ruggedness without coarseness. Quality bone is of particular importance in the breeding animal. Bold and dominating appearance in a male indicates prepotency or superiority of influence, though as in any breeding operation there is no certainty until the offspring can be judged.

Points of a beef heifer

The general points of a beef heifer are:

1 An attractive, feminine appearance, with good general balance. Outlook alert and intelligent, but showing no sign of nervousness. Good overall length, with head carriage denoting correct spinal structure. Top straight and firm, with underline parallel, showing ample but not excessive depth of body. Legs strong, well set on and well formed
2 Flesh firm and resilient but not 'blubbery'. Skin supple and mellow to the touch. Coat full, long and silky in winter and readily shed in summer
3 Rear end. Plenty of width and depth in quarters, showing fleshing carried well down second thigh to hock. Pin bones nicely set up and level; tail carriage smooth, without drooping or 'cocking'. The whole suggesting good construction for ease of calving; no pinched appearance
4 Hindquarters showing great length from hooks to pins (the area of expensive meat) and well fleshed throughout. Hip bones smoothly covered and not too prominent. Flank full and well let down. Correct construction in the hindquarters is of vital importance in the reproductive function of the female, and this area is also one of the most important beef areas

5 Head and shoulders. Placid open countenance with broad
   forehead and muzzle—a wide grass mower would be
   expected to give higher performance than a narrow one.
   Under-jaw strong but not protruding. Eyes set well apart,
   bold but soft and feminine. Shoulders wide, but smooth and
   not prominent; well covered and open, not dished between
   shoulder blades on top
6 Middle rib and fore-end. Deep, well sprung and evenly
   fleshed. Forelegs straight and cleanly set on. Brisket not too
   heavy, with no excessive dewlap

Colours

Aberdeen Angus The breed colour in Britain is black. Herds of
Red Angus exist in North America. White is objectionable
except on the underline behind the navel. A white cod (see
Glossary) on the bull is most undesirable.

Galloway Black with brownish tinge, or dun. Skin mellow and
moderately thick, hair soft and wavy, with mossy undercoat.
Wiry or curly hair is very objectionable. The Belted Galloway
has a wide and cleanly defined belt of white behind the
shoulders, the rest being black or dun.

Hereford and Polled Hereford White head and crest,
generally extending along neck-line, white underparts and
socks, white tail switch. No black on muzzle or horns. Rest of
body a deep rich red; any black hairs undesirable.

Highland From cream through brown and dark brindle to
black. A waxy tinge in the horn of a red brindle is said to denote
kindly feeding properties. There are two styles of horn in the
female, one slightly forward and upward and the other less
forward and back-swirling. A wide level sweep of horn is
preferred in bulls.

Shorthorn Red, white, red and white, or roan. White in large
splashes is not desirable. A bull's horns should be oval in shape,
creamy white in colour and waxy in texture. They should carry
their thickness right to the point.

Feeding

Animals for showing must be well forward for their age. Feeding before birth consists of maintaining the dam in fit enough condition to bear a healthy calf and follow with a sufficient supply of milk. Excessive condition is not required on any female at this stage; it may result in an over-large calf and a difficult birth.

Though selection of show stock may be delayed till the six-to-eight-month stage, any likely contenders are given favourable treatment as calves. A calf creep is a most important feature of any loose box or yard housing beef stock. A protein percentage of around 16 per cent is considered desirable, and in these busy times many feeders prefer to buy a proprietary compound, adjusting the ration with additions of cereal or sugar-beet pulp for less demanding classes of stock. An important point stressed by one feeder is the avoidance of urea in rations for calves under twelve months old. He lost one very promising heifer calf through bloat when on a urea diet.

The calf creep becomes a kind of foster mother to the youngsters. Set in the middle of a pasture, it is where they congregate to shelter from rough weather—and food is always to hand.

Throughout the rearing stage, best quality hay is offered. Not only must this be well made, but it should be from a meadow whose produce is particularly favoured by cattle and which do well on it. As an example, a pedigree Hereford breeder planned to plough a certain ley in due rotation. His cattleman asked him to hold his hand and plough out another instead as the threatened field yielded hay really appreciated by young stock. These are the lengths to which a successful show man must be prepared to go.

A further advantage of the creep feed is that it prevents a severe setback at weaning. When calves are thoroughly accustomed to hard feed and are seven or eight months old, weaning is little shock to them. They may bawl for their mothers for a couple of nights, but then settle down to lay on flesh. A medium plane of nutrition is recommended at this stage, with oats and sugar-beet pulp being added to the calf pencils. By soaking the beet pulp and then mixing it with the rest a most palatable ration is assured. Although stock do no better on oats than on barley, the oat is reckoned the safer food, and so is reserved for the more valuable show stock. For the fussy feeder, a barrel of treacle may be bought, but the 'magic' or 'secret' ration has less place in most show men's routine than formerly.

To gain firm flesh these 'secret' recipes may be used, but basically linseed cannot be surpassed for a combination of bloom and good fleshing. Although some feeders do not like beans, the consensus of opinion is in favour of them. Cod-liver oil is always included in winter rations.

At the yearling stage young beefs receive some 6–8lb (2.7–3.6kg) of concentrates daily, plus the best hay ad lib, plus a clean bed—*always* a dry, clean bed. The red breeds—Devon, Hereford, Lincoln Red, Sussex—may be housed during the day in summer to preserve their dark-red coats. Without doubt sunshine bleaches them, so they are turned out at night instead. In some countries a light red is preferred, but in Britain the dark red is the favourite. It is associated with vigour and strength.

As the beast matures, a maximum of 10–12lb (4.5–5.4kg) of concentrates daily is customary. Here the art of the feeder really comes into play. In these later stages cattle cannot be fed by a chart, but according to appetite. The cattleman watches closely, and at the slightest sign of lack of appetite he cuts down the feed or changes it to something more appetising to that particular animal. The commercial feeder can brook no such fastidiousness, but the exhibitor must be prepared to pander to individual idiosyncrasies. Some feeders even use a specially spiced mineral mixture, with aniseed incorporated to make it attractive, for their show animals. The cost is £5 against £1.50 for the same weight of standard mixture, and is yet another showing cost. Two feeds daily usually suffice. The late evening feed is given at the more critical times if it helps appetite. Wet sugar-beet pulp mixed with the concentrate ration is a good and safe appetiser.

Too much middle is not required in a beast destined for immediate slaughter. 'Butchers want only a fore-end and a back end; they don't want any middle,' is one comment. This emphasises the importance of the killing-out percentage, for an animal with a big gut will not kill out well. Rations for the purpose include 12–14 per cent protein and the balance in quality hay.

Schedules

The exhibitor must study schedules. Different breeds have different dates in the calendar to split classes by age. A Hereford bull born in August would be competing against bulls eleven months older when the division date is 1 September. This is obviously too much of a handicap, and stock born soon after the scheduled date are naturally preferred.

Although some calves are outstanding from birth, others mature later. A South Midlands exhibitor used to castrate at two weeks old all bull calves that he considered unfit for breeding or showing. Both he and his herdsman then found that they had steers that should have been bulls, and bulls that should be steers. They now wait till six or eight months before deciding finally.

Grooming

The most important thing about grooming is to start a long time before show day. For spring and summer shows, cattle are picked out the previous autumn. Their feet must be kept right. Large cattle foot clippers are useful, but be careful not to take off too much at once. A sharp wood chisel used with a downward stroke on to a wooden block makes a neat job in the right hands.

Control is essential, and a well-designed cattle crush is the show man's great ally—and almost as indispensable for commercial stock. It helps accurate foot trimming.

Washing begins as soon as the weather is reasonably warm in spring. A soaking with the hose-pipe is given, then a sham-

poo or wash with soap powder. A detergent shampoo/
vermin killer is diluted in warm water, and brushed in all over,
from head to foot. A rubber apron is an invaluable aid.
Washing, including a rub dry, may take an hour per animal.

The beast is washed once weekly right up to show day. The
day before the show, its tail is plaited, doubled up and wrapped
in a crêpe bandage. This keeps it clean in transit, and when the
bandage is removed at the show the tail hair falls out really
bushy and crimply. Machine clippers are used mainly on tail
and head, not along the spine as might be the case with a pen of
fat or store bullocks for the market.

Horns

These 'useless appendages', as they have been described, are
part of the charm of Highland and Longhorn cattle. They may
also be retained on quiet breeds such as Herefords, and at least
one Ayrshire breeder resolutely refuses to remove them,
averring that the whole character of the beast may be seen in the
horn. I have seen a pair from a champion Shorthorn of many
years ago that oozed quality. There is a lesson somewhere in
that the naturally selected Chillingham Wild White cattle all
have horns of perfect symmetry.

The exhibitor can enhance his animal by proper horn care.
Some weeks before the show, a medium-coarse grade of
sandpaper is used on them. When the roughness has gone a
finer grade is used, or a piece of broken glass is preferred by
some herdsmen. For the final finish, Vim, Gumption or Three-
in-One oil are used. On show day no sandpapering is done; a
little light oil is all that is needed.

Show day

On arriving at the show such dirt as may have been spread
on to the coat is removed, the animal bedded down, fed and left
to rest. No general washing is done. Light machine oil (half a
pint is enough for two animals) is rubbed over the skin with a
rag, or a spray used if preferred.

A clipped coat is easier to keep clean than a long one. Comb and scissors are used for the actual grooming, the scissors being offset or cranked at an angle. Hair is kept in place by a castor oil and water spray, and eucalyptus is a familiar smell in the Smithfield air. Although some people like to 'bone up' the hair into a series of ripples over the whole coat, others think it unnatural. Here is an American's advice on preparing cattle:

Breeds vary in hair length, and some have much shorter summer coats than winter ones, but showing with the hair up does make an enormous difference to a beast's appearance. Regular combing and brushing helps to train the hair to stand, either through curling the wet hair or by comb, brush and elbow grease. Curling is done by taking comb or curry comb, and waving the hair with a back and forth motion. Start on the topline, and go down the sides. Then the hair is turned up and brushed dry.

On the day before the show, extra time is spent grooming and working the hair dry. When show day dawns, an early rinse, soap and scrub is followed by working the hair until it is completely dry. Then let the beast relax, and the exhibitor too, to prepare him or herself mentally for stepping out into that magic circle.

An hour or so before the class is called, the animal is watered and its show halter put on. Next stage is 'boning', the action of combing up and working the hair to give a rugged appearance. A bar of saddle soap is useful here, put on with a downward motion, and the hair then combed up and worked.

Last job before entering the ring is a spray with grooming oil over the animal's coat. Make sure that a comb is carried in a pocket, for touching up whilst in the ring, and that any necessary documents and entry cards are taken. The best competitors heed any instructions from judge or steward, are courteous and helpful to other stockmen, and are gracious losers. Congratulating the winner should be automatic and, fortunately, usually is.

Breed sales

In addition to top-class beef stock shown at successive events throughout the season, a number are shown at breed sales. If they are good enough to stand among the best, buyers have an extra chance to look at them before they enter the actual sale ring. If these cattle win prizes, so much the better. Some high-class animals are shown only on such occasions, because their owners simply have not enough time to take them out more often.

As an example, a Scottish Borders farm has a herd of twelve White-bred Shorthorns and a herd of fifty Galloways, half of the latter being bred pure and the other half crossed with the White-bred Shorthorn to breed the well-known Blue-grey, in demand both as suckler dam and as feeder. This set-up is reproduced on hundreds of hill and marginal farms, though the actual breeds may differ.

The Galloways are bred mainly for females, the White-bred Shorthorns for males. Calving is timed partly by natural conditions and partly by sale dates. White-breds calve in the third quarter of the year, that is, July to September. Young bulls are sold at fifteen to eighteen months of age, at a season when suckler calf breeders seek a herd sire. The bull calves suckle their dams for the first nine months, after which they are box-fed at pasture twice a day. Three weeks before the sale they are brought in and fed three times a day. The ration is bulky rather than too rich. High protein is not needed; the object is to develop the rumen and persuade the cattle to consume as much as possible. This helps development, and a well-middled bull looks better as he parades the ring.

The bulls are taught to lead, preferably at a young age, in practice when the owner or herdsman has time to attend to them. They are shampooed by hand twice—a fortnight before the sale and again four days before. Daily grooming with curry comb and dandy brush is done for a month or so before sale, and the bulls are sheeted at night. This is an important operation, designed to prevent sweat accumulating and spoiling the appearance of the coat, and it is started some three weeks before the sale. A large hessian bag, such as a bran bag or sugar-beet pulp bag, forms an adequate sheet for the purpose. It will not be worn in public. Some cattle, like humans, sweat much more easily and profusely than others, and it may be necessary to keep the sheet on all the time. The sweat escapes through the holes in the sacking and the coat remains dry. If it becomes wet, cattle become itchy and start to rub hair off themselves.

The bulls are also walked for up to a mile once or, preferably, twice daily. This process not only helps muscle development but educates the animals. Before the sale, hoofs are scrubbed clean with soap and water in the case of the white bulls. Black Galloway hoofs are dressed with black shoe polish. Tails are washed and shaken out. The most is made of the Galloway's curly coat, but this is basically a matter of breeding. Unfortunately, well coated bulls do not always produce their like.

The Galloway sires are in most demand at twelve to fifteen months. Some buyers prefer a bull ready to work; others chance their judgement with a younger one and try him with a few cows before using him generally. The main sales for both White-bred Shorthorns and Galloways are in February and November. By splitting the Galloway herd into spring and autumn calving, bulls of the correct age are available for both sales.

Another type of show animal is the beef steer or heifer destined for the Christmas fatstock shows. Suckler calf sales in the North of England and Scotland are the happy hunting grounds for feeders whose farming hobby is the pursuit of a Smithfield rosette. Calves by Continental sires are popular, but the dam is equally important. Angus and Shorthorn on the female side is often sought for the necessary quality.

Three important factors are: the animal itself, its breeding and conformation; its quietness when circling the ring and especially when being handled by the judge; and its condition.

Even though a beef animal is due for slaughter next day, it must walk correctly. If a judge doesn't like a beast when he first sees it, the chances are that he never will.

Firmness of flesh is required. Fleshing should be even; soft patches and bumps denote fat. Covering of flesh on the tail head, sirloin and ribs is sought, while the brisket should be neat and small. The cod (see Glossary) should be firm, but with the rubber ring method of castration there may be little cod to assess.

Simmentals in the sunshine: only one bull in this class walked with a staff, and there is much sense in the belief that bulls in need of a staff are of a temperament unsuited either to a showground or to being bred from. The switch on the tail of the foreground bull is a wonderful example of the art of bringing out nature's endowments; leather head collars are used

Early morning scene before spectators arrive. The comradeship of the showing world is one of its most pleasant aspects. Though judges may be, and often are, criticised, the novice exhibitor will be helped by old hands if the right approach is made. Five o'clock on judging morning will find preparations in full swing, and a walk at that hour has a flavour of its own

Soap and water for this Friesian heifer while a Shorthorn bull waits his turn for grooming. Special washing areas are provided at major shows, but exhibitors must provide their own buckets and cleaning equipment. After washing, cattle are walked smartly to prevent a chill before returning to their stalls

Cow and calf is always a popular class. A light rope halter is adequate for the youngster, while the mother has a showy leather headstall – such details enhance an animal's appearance

5   Cattle—Dairy

Timing

As with other classes of stock, preparing dairy cattle for show starts months before the event. In the case of a newly-calven cow, her calving must be timed for a particular show—it is unrealistic to expect a cow in this category to win at a succession of major events right through the summer. If a cow is required for the Royal Show in the first week of July, she must be served to calve with enough time to settle down and come to full milk in late June. The ideal period for most dairy breeds is two weeks before the show, although in the case of a breed with a very tight and blocky udder—the Ayrshire—a shorter period may be desirable.

Colostrum flow should have ceased and undue 'wedging' (see Glossary) disappeared. In the case of a dry cow or in-calf heifer, the future calving date is not so critical and some dairymen prefer to exhibit these classes of cattle rather than risk upsetting a first-class milker. As we shall see, proper management minimises risk to the deep milker.

Feeding

For several months before major shows, stock should sleep in at nights. Feeding is done with the greatest care, and here the herdsman's own recipes come into play. However, let no one be dissuaded from showing because he doesn't know any special feeds; effect is marginal compared with a good standard ration, and the show man can start to experiment later. The aim at all times is to bring the animal to peak condition for a particular show. This is not easy, but it is better to err on the side of caution, and present the beast in rising rather than falling bodily condition.

A newly-calven cow must continue her milking ration of fairly high protein right up to the show, but in the case of other cattle, feeds of sweet hay only may be used for the preceding two days. Then the dung tightens up, and the animal steps out of the waggon looking clean and smart. Loose dung swished all over itself and its neighbours by a beast upset by the journey is a cattleman's nightmare.

Clipping and washing

Clipping cattle is done well in advance of show day. Skilful clipping brings out the best points of a beast; unskilled work makes an awful mess. It is wrong to begin at the head, especially with a bull. He is upset at the start, and remains that way throughout the operation. Begin at the hind foot, work upwards towards the thigh, curving away to the tail root when halfway up the thigh. The tail is clipped as far as the switch, a most important and showy part. The switch is the collection of long hairs guarding the tail tip, and a dazzling white switch sets off an animal beautifully.

From the tail root, take one cut the full width of the shears for the full length of the spine. Glide out on either side on reaching the shoulders. This spine cut smartens an animal considerably, and helps control of skin parasites. It seems to indicate a man who is proud of his stock. Start again at the front hoofs, working upwards. All the neck, head and ears are clipped. For show clipping, a fine shearing head is essential; a rough one will never give the desired finish.

A separate small cow-shed with neck ties is a considerable advantage for show preparation. Here the washing and clipping take place without upsetting herd routine. Though the main wash is done on the day before the event, the successful show man's rule is to keep his stock clean at all times. A white Shorthorn cow was regularly brought out at local shows in immaculate condition. 'How do you keep her so clean?' asked a lady bystander. 'I never let her get dirty, ma'am!' responded the proud herdsman. That is the essence of showing stock, for to take an untutored, dung-stained animal from the field and expect it to become a show beast in a matter of hours is hopeless. The prospective show animal receives extra attention throughout, and this care permeates the whole herd and lifts the general level of management.

The first step in washing is to thoroughly soak the animal, using cold water from a hose-pipe. This soaking takes several minutes. Then take buckets of clean, warm water, and pour on liberally from the tip of the nose to the tip of the tail, first along one side, then the other. Do this carefully; it is easy to miss patches.

A proprietary detergent in warm water is used next. Three or four buckets are necessary, and the animal is brushed briskly all over. Done properly, this is hard work. Ears and eyes are cleaned with a damp cloth. The final stage is to wash off the detergent with cold water, and then to walk the beast in the open air so that it does not catch cold. In the case of a milk cow, the udder is thoroughly dried.

Horns and hoofs

Not many cattle have horns left on these days, though in breeds such as Highland and Longhorn they are a vital characteristic. The neck of a broken bottle scraped on the horn leaves a marvellous finish. There are various horn training devices on the market, though these were most commonly used on breeds where dehorning is now general. A few drops of linseed oil or other 'secret' recipes may be used to bring out the full beauty of horn, one of nature's loveliest substances—witness shepherds' crooks and walking-sticks fashioned from ram, cow or deer horn.

Hoofs are oiled with pig oil. Only rarely does a good foot need trimming provided that exercise and housing, and above all breeding, have been correct. Sound feet are essential in any stock, and to attempt to manicure basically unsound feet is to defeat the whole object of showing, which is to lift the general level of livestock production. The careful breeder ranks sound feet and mouths among his first considerations.

Final touches

Pig oil is also used on black patches in cattle, especially where this is required to contrast with white, as in Friesians. White underparts, especially the udder, are chalked just before entering the ring, to enhance their pure colour. Tail switches are washed with soapy water, all dung accumulations being removed, then swished thoroughly to dry them.

Where these preparations are done thoroughly, and cattle carefully loaded and unloaded, show-day work should be confined to a final polish. Eight assorted bulls, cows and heifers were transported from the Ironside herd of British Friesians near York to a show ninety miles away. When they arrived, two buckets of water sufficed to clean the lot.

Milking

In the case of a milking class, the cow should be milked twelve hours previously. If the show is at noon, the cow should be milked at midnight the night before. On such points as these the dedicated stockman scores. Those who read this book may learn from the experts; they still have to go to bed late and rise early to put the knowledge into practice.

The sealing of teats to prevent milk dripping is wrong, and is one of the practices that give showing a bad name, for it is harmful to subsequent milk production. If one quarter is lighter than the others, the cow may be held in such a way as to lighten the fault, and that is part of the art of showmanship. But a conscientious herdsman would give up showing rather than indulge in practices known to be harmful to his stock.

Stance

Correct stance is taught while exercising. In dairy cattle, the front feet should be level with each other and slightly apart; the rear ones placed one slightly in front of the other. Front and rear feet should be the correct distance apart—that which shows the topline to best advantage. If too close, the back will be humped; if too stretched, it will sag in the middle. This correct positioning is best studied at the show-ring, as are the correct techniques for arriving at it. The animal is taught to stand steady, then pulled slightly forward, or pushed slightly back, until the most advantageous spacing is achieved. An animal that has learnt to stand correctly saves much nervous energy, both its own and its handler's, while in the ring.

An important point is never to give up showing while in the ring until the awards have actually been handed out. Cattle have been placed at the top of the line from the start of judging, lulling their handler into a careless attitude dreaming of the cup about to be presented. Another beast still being shown correctly and smartly then catches the judge's eye, and is moved up above the slack exhibitor.

Headgear

For in-calf heifers, a clean white halter is best. On cows and bulls, a leather halter is generally deemed smarter and more serviceable; a bull certainly looks more the part in a leather halter. Really good leather halters are hard to find. One breeder bought some Canadian ones of brown leather, and had his local saddler copy them. Without a doubt, a neat and tidy halter helps that well turned-out look.

Bulls

A strap chain attached to a leather halter (see page 18) is generally deemed the most effective for a bull. Staffs indicate that the bull is unmanageable without their use, and if a bull turns, the herdsman cannot hold him if he means to go. 'A bull that needs a staff shouldn't be in a show-ring,' said one herdsman.

Though bulls can never totally be trusted, they like to trust their handler. This apparent contradiction is understood by any cattleman, for kindness and firmness are the twin bastions of successful handling of any animal. A contented, well-managed bull is not for ever tugging at his ring. I saw one ring that had been in the bull's nose for a year, and had not pulled a hole large enough to see. Other bulls work at their rings so continuously that a sizeable hole appears.

The faster a bull walks under control, the better he looks in the show-ring. Too many are poor walkers. Any lowering of standards in this direction is to the detriment of the breed. Foot faults are among those that are much easier to get into than to get out of, and the show-ring serves a useful purpose if it sets a standard in this respect.

6   Lowland Sheep

To have to tell a youngster that his or her sheep are not good enough to show is disheartening. They must start with what they have got, and the show-ring will bring home deficiencies sooner than anything. Then a start in the right direction can be made.

Points of one's chosen breed must be learnt. The best stock are usually inbred or line bred to some extent (see Glossary). Both are rather loose terms, the best definition of which is probably the old saw: 'It's line breeding when it works, and inbreeding when it doesn't!' Female to grandsire is as close as most people breed, and then only provided both sides are absolutely sound. Any inherited faults or weaknesses are intensified by inbreeding.

'Two out and one in' is an accepted breeding method. By this is meant two out-crosses to unrelated stock, followed by a mating carrying related blood in the next generation. This is not the place for detailed breeding schemes, but no work on preparation for show and sale can ignore the material to be fashioned. Showing is the art of bringing out the best in a good animal, not an attempt to deceive with poor, badly bred stock.

Feeding

Although cattle may either be housed and have all feed provided, or graze supplemented grass, sheep require rather different treatment. The ideal is to provide a succession of succulent green crops right through the summer show season, as well as the correct winter feed. Fortunately, the areas involved are not large, for these crops can be very expensive.

On the average mixed lowland farm, sheep are part of the system. Maiden 'seeds' or one-year ryegrass and clover mixtures form the basis of grazing for show stock, supplemented by two- and three-year leys providing both grazing and a hay crop. Hay is invariably the basic winter feed.

At some shows green material may be provided by the organisers; at others the stockman must take his own. In any event, the show sheep are housed more than the commercial flock while preparations are under way, and because of this an acreage of easily mown, succulent green material is essential. A mixture of vetches (tares) and oats is the traditional and still unsurpassed means of providing fresh summer green food. Sown at 12–14 stones (76.2–88.9kg) per acre in 1 stone (6.3 kg) of oats, the proportions of peas and vetches may be varied according to the price of seed, which will certainly be very dear. It will be the most expensive crop the farmer grows, but the cost of the small acreage can be offset against the chance of winning the Bath and West or the Highland.

Rye and ryegrass are another possiblity for spring and early summer but are not quite as good—and nothing but the best will do for this job. One leading Suffolk sheep exhibitor grows one acre of peas and vetches for a string of about twenty-five show sheep.

To follow the spring and early summer flush of growth is not easy. Cabbages provide one answer, sown as early as possible, which may not be until March or even early April in some areas. Over a thousand cabbages are loaded on to one transport carrying some twenty rams to the Kelso sales in late summer. Early-maturing varieties are sought, but even these are too immature for the early shows. Cabbages cut on the previous day are preferable to fresh ones, and a great virtue of this crop is its ability to keep fresh for several days after cutting.

Another good feed for later grazing is the rape/kale hybrid, which lasts longer than the English variety. The latter tends to bolt if rain follows a dry spell, curtailing its usefulness. From the New Year onwards, mangolds are an unexcelled succulent food for show sheep. They are easily transported, and the previous year's crop has been stored till late July in the North. This was achieved by storing a good depth of mangolds under a shed with plentiful straw cover.

For concentrates, a simple mix of oats and barley plus a little high protein suffices. Sheep exhibitors do not seem to rely on 'secret' feed formulas to the extent found in the cattle world.

Timing

For show sheep, lambing dates tend to be rather earlier than for commercial stock. Cluns may be brought forward from March to early February to gain that extra lamb growth, and it is generally accepted that the best Suffolks are often born in the last week in December, even though 1 January is the official start of the new lambing season.

Breeders of Down sheep can spot potential prize-winners at birth, whereas with other breeds this is not so often achieved. The smartest Clun lambs may not turn out the best, so lambs for the yearling ewe shows are not picked till September.

When Smithfield or the Christmas fatstock shows are the aim, June lambing must be considered. This is by no means contrary to good sheep husbandry; ewe lambs may be tupped to lamb in this month and provide excellent, neat little lambs to catch the judge's eye five or six months hence.

Breeds

Hill Cheviot, Exmoor Horn, Welsh Halfbred and other smaller breeds frequently figure in the Smithfield cross-bred lamb's pedigree. Of 80 pens of Butchers' Weight lambs entered at a recent Royal Smithfield Show, Suffolk appears in the first and second generation pedigrees listed 69 times; Southdown, 16, of which 5 are in the 210lb (95.3kg) and under class (for 3 lambs); Dorset Down, 10; Dorset Horn, 3; Hampshire Down, 3; Welsh Halfbred, 4; Welsh Mountain, 8; Cheviot, 14 (the Smithfield catalogue is ambiguous regarding the type of Cheviot); Welsh Speckle-faced, 4; Kerry Hill, 2; Clun Forest, 3; Blue-faced Leicester/Swaledale (Mule), 4; Charmoise, 1; Friesland/Romney, 1; and Ryeland, 1.

Dipping

'Well dipped is half trimmed,' Jack Bulmer, exhibitor of Smithfield Supreme Champion lambs, once remarked, and indeed correct dipping is vital to the show sheep. One successful exhibitor uses Young's Show Dip and Young's Blue Label in 50:50 proportions. Soft water or water that has been softened is advised, and it is essential that the powder be really dissolved. A pleasant, breezy day is better than hot sun, and the aim is to have the sheep dry within three hours. After that they run out at pasture, but have shelter if they need it. When schedules allow, a dip is given between each show, though when two multi-day shows follow each other in successive weeks, as with the Royal and the Great Yorkshire, this is not possible. Dipping removes grease and dirt, and freshens the sheep's appearance.

Trimming and carding

No two men trim alike. Each develops his own individual style according to his ideal of the perfect sheep. Jack Bulmer once trimmed a Suffolk for fellow Yorkshire competitor Tom Midgeley. 'You could turn that sheep among your own now, and it would match them,' said the latter. An Irish exhibitor took photos from all angles to try and copy the shaping of Jack Bulmer's Malton Suffolks. True artists like Harry Boast, son-in-law of famous Suffolk shepherd Harold Rusk, could create optical illusions when their sheep took the ring. The Benacre flock became almost the fountain-head of the Suffolk world after Harold Rusk moved there.

The golden rule in trimming is: 'It's not what you cut off that counts; it's what you leave on.' A skilled trimmer removes the minimum, but in the right places. Hand shears are the general rule, although some block off the backs by machine. Heavy shears for initial stages and much lighter ones for final trimming are best.

Although it is possible to prepare a sheep only a few days before a show, the more usual period to start is four to six weeks beforehand. The first stage is to level the backs, in the case of a Shortwool, leaving a quarter to half an inch of wool if starting a month or more before show day. If the period is shorter, obviously more wool must be left.

A dipping is then given before starting the next stage—carding. This operation copies the textile industry's technique of dealing with wool. Carding wire may be bought by the yard, or ready for use in a 'board'. It consists of a mass of fine wires with turned tips that catch the wool and 'lift' it. Fairly heavy boards are best, with a slightly convex curve. Leather-backed carding wire can cost over £30 a yard, but some rubber-backed material is being tried at less than half the price.

A flat card is used for 'scratching' or patting the fleece level, while the lifting card is bevelled. Both must be sharp, so sharp that they are painful to hold on the business side. The fleece is scratched down to remove dirt, then lifted by means of a circular action. The wool so lifted is damped down, then clipped off. When lifting, sweep *against* the fall of the wool. To clean the carder, an old dinner fork with prongs bent at right angles is the best weapon.

Faces are clipped out to leave a clear line between wool and face skin, the position of which varies with the different breeds. As the head cannot be clipped effectively when a halter is worn, the Y-shaped yoke on a stand to take the sheep's jaws is a useful tool.

Although some sheep lead on the halter naturally, others must be taught. Leather halters are fashionable for some breeds; white cotton ones for others. Halters can be made in white nylon, but tend to chafe the skin. Generally speaking, synthetics and animals do not mix.

When the final trimming is done at home, the sheep is sheeted down to keep it clean for the show, If it doesn't satisfy its shepherd at home, it certainly never will on exhibition. Once there, the animal-loving general public makes life difficult, as head scratching and patting of the fleece cause a considerable amount of extra work. When people pay to go to a show, it seems rather mean to bar them from touching the animals at all, but the usual system of penning behind low hurdles leaves scope for unwarranted interference.

Numbering

Whether for show or sale, the individual numbering of close-wool sheep must be done precisely. Few things detract more from an animal's appearance than a series of numbers slapped on indiscriminately. Cellulose paint is used, and red is a popular colour. Care must be taken to see that correct catalogue order is followed, and that painted numbers correspond with ear tags. When a series of sheep make up one consignment, concentration is necessary or mistakes will be made.

The sequence of branding irons should be set in numerical order on a table in reach of the marker but safe from the sheep. The paint tin stands at one end. The face of the iron should be round for sheep in wool, flat for those close-clipped. Numbering is one of the last jobs done before transporting, and opportunity may be taken to wash the sheep's backside with clean water and a stiff brush. Sheep travel better when fairly empty, and at this stage the slightly wilted cabbage is a useful food.

In the ring

When in the ring, keep one eye on the judge and the other on the sheep. If the judge is not looking in your directon that is no excuse for slip-shod handling, because other people are watching. Among them may be potential customers or the judges at some future shows, having a preview. Nor can one be sure when a Press photo is being taken—a golden opportunity to advertise one's goods.

White coats are obligatory for handlers, and a smart appearance can only enhance the general picture. 'Never let down your stock by your own slip-shod appearance' is a golden rule for all exhibitors.

7 Hill Sheep

The exhibitor of hill sheep must keep the commercial man in mind at all times. Of all farm stock, hill sheep are bred to live with least assistance in a certain, rather hard environment. Survival in storm is an essential attribute in this class of stock; without it, all else is worthless, so animals are selected to that end.

A bright, bold eye is sought in the hill ram. He is the leader of a flock of fifty, sixty or seventy ewes and he must scent danger and lead them from it. The bold eye denoting courage in adverse conditions is no mere fad. Though ultimately all hill sheep or their offspring end on the butcher's table, the placid disposition indicating good food conversion in the lowland sheep has no place on the hills. Unless the sheep can stay alive, there will be no conversion at all.

Nor can lambing dates be varied greatly to bring out early-born, quickly matured lambs for the autumn sales. Hill rams should be reared on hill ground at least as hard as that they will run on as adults, and the rearing of Scottish Blackfaces, for example, on forward, sheltered farms does the breed no service at all. Cheviot, North of England and Welsh hill sheep breeders have not developed this habit.

Because of such factors, hill sheep are shown in a more 'natural' condition than most classes of stock, but nevertheless well repay some little time spent in making the most of them, whether for show or sale.

Age and numbers

There is an increasing tendency to trade in ram lambs. Too much forcing with high protein feed defeats its own object, for such 'boiled up' lambs are not highly regarded by either judge or buyer. A little trimming and tidying round the head and neck, following a careful dipping, is all that is usually required.

The shearling ram is the one most commonly shown or sold. No ram breeder worth his salt will select other than from his best ewes, and as a fairly large choice is generally available only those with correct breed points and outstanding conformation are retained.

We have seen that lambing dates are unlikely to be altered. They may have become traditional on a particular holding for a century or more. Variations have been tried from time to time but, after one or two costly experiments, most farms revert to the original choice, and will continue to do so unless our climate changes radically.

Skilled breeders leave three times as many ram lambs uncastrated as they eventually hope to sell or retain for stock purposes. Depending on the method of castration, selected potential stock sheep are marked at a few days or weeks of age, or even at birth. They are then run with their dams along with the rest of the flock till weaning. After this, it is usual in upland districts to graze the ram lambs on meadow aftermath, so that nutrition is adequate to allow growth potential to be expressed. The ewe or gimmer lambs return to the hill after weaning, and may rejoin their dams even though they no longer suckle them. Their hefting instinct comes into play, and they learn heft boundaries from their dams, but as the ram lambs will be used on unrelated stock, hefting does not apply in their case.

Wintering

The year draws to a close and the lambs become hoggs, or tegs in the South. They winter on meadows, often with a traditional stone-built barn to provide shelter and keep dry the quality hay and limited amount of concentrates fed. These barns are better without doors so that the sheep simply run in and out as it suits them, and there is no danger of a door blowing shut and imprisoning the stock. Such happenings have brought tragedy in their wake.

Clipping

In May the hoggs return to the hill. They are clipped well before the main flock, probably in June, to give their coats that little extra time to grow before the summer shows or autumn sales. The shepherd takes care to make a specially tidy job of these animals which are by now his pride and joy. The sheep are not clipped too short, and no unsightly tags are left. Then the shearling rams return to their high pastures, probably having had their numbers further depleted as the shears revealed defects of conformation.

Sale rams—housing and feeding

Some five weeks before the summer shows, individual rams may be brought down and given special attention, but these summer shows are not to be compared with the serious business of the ram sales and the shows that accompany them. Most hill ram sales are held from mid-September to late October, and as the days shorten so the risk increases of the rams breaking out and straying among ewes where they have no business. Ram paddocks are the best fenced fields on the farm. The danger of rams fighting among themselves also increases.

Weather in the few weeks before the autumn sales is very variable. Every effort is made to keep the fleeces dry and so sale rams are usually housed at night, and during the day in bad weather. This short period of pampering does not affect their hardiness; it is simply to ensure that they do not enter the sale ring in a wet and bedraggled state, and drop in value for the sake of a little care. A sheep that is accustomed to confinement is also more at home in the sale ring; one that has never been in a building before is hardly likely to look his best in the hubbub, lights and the general clamour that hill men generate on the rare occasions they meet.

In this pre-sale period some concentrates are fed, but the amount should not exceed $\frac{1}{2}$lb (227g) per day, and should be limited to a mixture of bran, sugar beet pulp or other cereals, and a little concentrated compound sheep feed. 'Be cautious—don't overdo it' is the experienced hill shepherd's advice. Better to have the sheep in improving condition rather than 'over the top'. Most hill sheep farmers are professionals, or they employ a shepherd who is, and would not dream of buying a ram without his advice. They know well enough if a sheep has been over-fed for the conditions it must face.

Care of feet

Not much can be done to a sheep's feet, other than to keep them sound. They can't be polished like a bull's. Rams especially, however, have a deplorable habit of going lame just when needed. They remain sound throughout spring and summer, then tend to be neglected through the rush of early autumn work and when taken up have misshapen hoofs. My vet tells me that every autumn he is faced with a rush of frantic farmers who have suddenly realised that the tup sales and tupping time are upon them, and that the tups are stumbling about with feet like footballs! It shouldn't happen, but it does.

A periodic run through the footbath, or a squirt from a spray into *every* foot (not just those suspected of lameness) is the surest way to keep the feet right. When tups have this amount of attention, any excess growth of horn is noted and trimmed immediately.

Cleaning, bloom dips

Two weeks before sale or show, the rams are given a shampoo of a proprietary mixture and clean water. The shampoo is scrubbed well in by hand. A brisk day is chosen if possible, and the animal dried quickly.

A point that has arisen recently in connection with anti-scab dips is water temperature. The powder does not dissolve properly until the water in the dip reaches a certain temperature, which may not be until a number of sheep have gone through. Improperly dissolved powder leaves a dip stain or tint on the tips of the fleeces. This is a source of loss to the

Grand Parade at the East of England: Charolais advance in single file as part of a display which passes the Royal Box at the centre of the stand. Among cattle, yearlings are those most likely to cause trouble *(East of England Agricultural Society)*

Grandfather and granddaughter combine to put finishing touches on this Derbyshire Gritstone that went on to win the breed championship

Use of the carder and brush to bring out the best in a Leicester sheep. This sheep has one of the heaviest fleeces among British breeds, and the coils of wool should be the thickness of a finger. All breeds have their special points

Suffolk sheep in the Untrimmed class. The shearsman has less chance to show his skills, but the true outline and wool qualities are more easily seen. Squaring the tail is the only clipping allowed in this class

main flock and obviously cannot be risked with sheep of high value. Until the problem is overcome, it is better to add hot water to the bath and ensure that the powder is fully dissolved.

More long standing is the issue of bloom dips. Rams of some breeds—Border Leicesters and Blackfaces especially—are dipped in a substance that turns the fleece any hue between yellow and bright orange. The British Wool Marketing Board does not like the practice, and down-grades the wool, but the value of one fleece does not deter a vendor, especially as the clip will not be his. Bloom dipping has nothing to commend it. The buyer suffers next summer when his fleeces are graded, but the eye-catching colour still seems to persuade him that here is an extra good sheep. A section of the sheep industry would like to see bloom dips banned altogether.

Some white wools take on a slight blueness associated with grazing on a certain type of peat. To combat this, a slight colouring by hand from a weak red clay solution is one remedy. Among greyer wools, a peat dip gives uniformity, and leaves the impression that the sheep have come off high ground, as indeed they usually have. Nothing could be cheaper than a bag of peat to colour the dip.

At the sale

Rams are given individual treatment on the way into the ring. For white-faced breeds, chalk blocks of the type used at dog shows and bought at pet shops are used to touch up faces and give a glistening white. A wipe round with a clean rag first helps in achieving that cared-for look that impresses buyers. Bidders are beguiled into paying a fair price for a good article; if the animal beneath the dressing is sub-standard, it is up to them to spot the fact, but a breeder who is careless with his stock throughout the year cannot redeem himself by extra work just before a show or sale.

Rams may be trained to stand quietly, though few shepherds have time to teach them. The best lessons are at summer shows, following which rams tend to behave themselves when on view.

Those sheep that, in the vendor's judgement, will make most money are usually put at the top of the sale list. Entries are made some time beforehand, with individual numbers in the case of pedigree sheep. Though it is not essential to show one's sheep in catalogue order, to bring them in haphazardly is misleading to buyers who may not hear the auctioneer's cry as he calls out the lot number.

'Try the better ones at the beginning' is general advice. They attract most bidders, and the unsuccessful ones will, we hope, bid further down the line. A really good top sheep or two give a favourable impression of the flock. If the outstanding sheep are left to the end, buyers may well refrain from bidding for the others in the hope of getting what they really want. Even the most experienced stockmen are proved wrong in this ordering business, when an animal which they didn't think very much about was the one that attracted the buyers' attention. In the case of numerically small breeds especially, an exceptional ram may attract few bids simply because he is too closely related to stock already held by the main buyers.

No more than an hour or two is spent in total in preparing each hill ram. No time is better spent; those final touches can make a lot of difference to the price of an animal herded regularly for one and a half or two and a half years.

Draft ewes

At least one-third of the average hill sheep farmer's income is from his draft ewes. These are ewes that have spent four or five years on the hill, and are now being sold while still in mid-breeding life. To the uninitiated, the point must be made that the draft ewe is not a throw-out; she is taking her place in the well tried system of sheep stratification, whereby older hill ewes are drafted down the hill to kinder conditions, to breed lambs by one of the various 'crossing' rams, usually Border or Blue-faced Leicester, Teeswater or Wensleydale.

Draft ewes should be shown in as good bloom as possible. They have summered on the hill, milking at least one lamb the while. The better they have milked, the leaner they are likely to be, yet the buyer may tup them earlier than if they had remained at home, and he wants them fit enough to produce twins in plenty. He may have a month or less to bring them into the desired condition; if they start too lean, they are unlikely to breed twins that year.

There is another reason for making the best of the various pens of draft ewes. Tup buyers take a good look at ewes and ewe lambs on sale. The drafts are the hill man's real shop window. They have weathered the storms, bred the lambs, yielded the wool clips. It may be possible to bring out an occasional eye-catching ram from a moderate stock, but the knowing breeder looks at the older dams. If they have come through four or five years in good order, little is likely to be wrong either with them, their management or their offspring.

The ewes receive much the same attention as the rams, but on a lesser scale. They will be clipped with the main flock, though if circumstances permit they are not left till last. Their feet are watched for lameness, they are marked carefully and not more than is essential for identification. The new owner may wish to put his own mark on; he must have room to do so.

Well before the sale and show date, these older ladies are examined thoroughly. A warranty will be given that they are sound 'above and below'—in teeth and udder. Any that are not *must* be sold separately and the faults admitted, otherwise the vendor will face reparations and a bad name. No auctioneer likes to receive complaints of sheep not being up to warranty.

While the examination is in progress, the ewes are matched for size and type. The object is to suit the buyer, who seeks sheep to mate with a certain ram. He will want them as alike as possible. Usually the best breed type are drawn into the first pen, followed by others as near perfection as possible. Then comes a pen of big, strong ewes with colour markings not quite as required. In breeds like the Swaledale, Dalesbred, Lonk, Gritstone or Blackface, the general run of ewes may be matched for face colour, first those too dark and then those too light. At the end comes a mixed bag of ewes not good enough to produce further breeding stock, but perfectly capable of throwing grand fat lambs to a Down ram.

'Uncrossed' ewes are those straight from the hill, used only for breeding pure replacements. 'Crossed' ewes may come from the same farm, but have been used to breed halfbred lambs for one or more years. Each class may do its next job equally well, but the fact must be stated.

Often pens are made up in tens. In districts of bigger flocks, bigger pens are customary, or the day's sale would be long drawn out. A Dumfriesshire farmer still sells in lots of forty-five, the number of Hill Cheviots that went into a railway wagon, though it is many years since sheep from that farm travelled by rail. The corresponding number for lambs was sixty.

8 Shearing Contests

'The shearing of sheep is an object of very considerable importance in rural economy,' said Youatt in *The Complete Grazier*, 1852. Earlier still, sheep shearings had become directly linked with forward-looking agricultural practice —witness the Holkham and Woburn gatherings of farmers and landowners from Britain and overseas.

Competitive shearing has developed into a spectator sport. If Britain does not yet match New Zealand in this aspect, ground is at least being gained, and the staging of the Golden Shears awards at the Royal Bath and West Show stands comparison with any similar event in the world. One busy Northumbrian farmer shears his neighbours' sheep by contract simply to tune himself up for competitions!

The contests are of two types—one is based on speed, the other on quality. The Golden Shears can only be won by a very fast shearer, and ten sheep in fifteen or sixteen minutes is the sort of achievement needed, with most finalists finishing within twenty minutes.

In the different systems of marking for speed, the fastest shearer may set the standard, and all finishing after him have marks deducted. In quality competitions at local level, a reasonable time of perhaps twelve minutes to shear two sheep is allowed, competitors being penalised or disqualified if they have not finished in the stipulated time. In no other farming operation is the difference between the top-class operator and the average so clearly marked.

Early days

The truly remarkable advances obtained by a combination of highly efficient machines and adroit professional handling are highlighted by an excerpt from the History of the Bath and West:

The competitions for the sheep-shearing premiums were popular occasions and remarkable feats were achieved. In June 1815, it took Abraham Ford, 'who sheared his sheep in the best style of workmanship', 1 hour 33 minutes to shear his three sheep. The second premium went to Thomas Tyley, who took 1 hour 46½ minutes, and the third to Samuel Scrivens, who took 1 hour 39 minutes, 'but in an inferior degree of excellence.' On this occasion they also gave a gratuity of 7s 6d to James Weeks, 'for his attendance and laudable Attempt at Improvement', and 'a lad named Tyley, about 12 years of age, for exemplifying great dexterity in winding up the fleeces,' received a special gratuity of 5s.

Three years previously, in 1812, the Society's 'coat and buttons' was awarded for expertise in sheep rearing, and the design of a horned sheep over a horse plough could not be bettered today.

Points

At the Royal Bath and West Bi-centenary Show points in the Young Farmers' Club machine shearing contest (two sheep) were:

Handling, shearing and condition of fleece	60
Appearance of sheep, including absence of skin cuts	30
Wrapping of fleece	10
	100

In the Open championship, two sheep were shorn by machine by competitors of any age, and points were:

Handling, shearing and condition of fleece	40
Appearance of sheep, including absence of skin cuts	40
Wrapping of fleece	20
	___
	100
	___

The time limit for both classes was ten minutes. Competitors exceeding the limit were disqualified, and the time allowed included catching from pens, shearing of sheep, penning after shearing and tying-up of fleeces.

Gang shearing marks were:

Time	25
Appearance of sheep (NB up to 20 points can be deducted by a Board Judge for double cutting)	50
Wrapping of fleece	25
	___
	100
	___

Time will be taken at the moment the shearing and wrapping is completed and the competitors are standing by the wrapped fleeces. The overall fastest time will gain a maximum of twenty-five points. Half a point will be deducted from other teams for every ten seconds or part of ten seconds of extra time taken.

The Golden Shears World Sheep Shearing competition takes a maximum of two top-class shearers from each competing country. Each competitor shears a maximum of ten sheep in the eliminating heats, and a maximum of fifteen in the final. Marking is:

Time	80
Handling and workmanship	50
Appearance of sheep	70
	200

The overall fastest time gains maximum points. Each competitor finishing after the quickest has points deducted. In 'Handling and Workmanship', every shearer starts with maximum points. Points are deducted for second cuts, for belly wool and neck wool not being broken out and if the shearer loses control of the sheep on the board, thereby upsetting the fleece. Concerning 'Appearance of Sheep', absence of cuts, tassels left on and general appearance are taken into account. Sheep are judged as a pen and a mark of merit awarded out of seventy points.

Competitors may be penalised if they do not use the full width of the shearing handpiece. This is obvious time-wasting, and denotes lack of prowess. Handpieces are designed to work at maximum capacity, and their correct setting is one of the shearer's skills.

Although some examples of scales of points are given here, the competitor must familiarise him or herself with the rules for each show. Prizes vary from the nominal to £1,500 divided among the first three in the Golden Shears World Championship. Money rewards do not end there, for the top men are engaged on tours and demonstrations at quite high fees. Yet they all started at the bottom, and that is a very good reason for treating the village show competition as a step towards the Golden Shears.

For many years wool was the most precious commodity per pound weight produced on British farms. Though it may now have been overtaken by meat, it is still well worth caring for, and shearing competitions are designed to that end.

In the absence of a national system of points, the following scale provides a popular basis:

Handling of sheep	25
Condition of fleece and wrapping	20
Absence of skin cuts, general appearance	30
Absence of double cutting	25
	100

Judging varies from one judge overseeing six competitors in local contests, to the Golden Shears standard of one to one, with an extra judge to enable the rest to move on a place when indicated by the timekeeper. At no time in that competition is any shearer not being watched by a judge. At the stipulated time each judge moves on to the next of the eight competitors, leaving behind his judging card for the next judge to mark up.

Methods

Godfrey Bowen did a marvellous job for the sheep industry when he toured sheep areas and left behind a chain of shearers not only skilled in his method, but able to teach it. The Bowen method undoubtedly speeded up and improved operations on the farm, and his contribution to a systematic approach to and control of the sheep is incalculable, but opinion differs on whether it is the best method for quality shearing.

Some judges believe that the orthodox two-handed shearing gives best result. In this method the belly and neck are opened up, then the shearer sweeps along one side exactly to the backbone, following along the other side using his other hand, and meeting exactly on the spine. In the Bowen method, one blow is given beyond the spine, and one side of the sheep is shorn downhill, ie with the wool falling away from the shears. With the two-handed method the wool always falls towards the shears, and the two sides are done exactly alike. The rules do not stipulate any particular method.

Wrapping the fleece is a section where points are unnecessarily lost. Contract shearers seldom wrap their own fleeces. They are therefore out of practice when mounting the competition boards, yet a fifth of the points may be at stake. Wrapping should be done by flinging out the fleece on to the floor or wrapping table, skin side downwards for most breeds, then flipping the sides inwards. Rolling starts at the breech, is done as tightly as possible and the whole fleece wrapped in a band twisted from the neck. Each fleece will be handled several times on its way to the mill; the shearer must ensure that it starts in proper shape.

Judges like to see a sheep clipped cleanly, and this applies particularly to the hindquarters. The object here is to ensure that the animal will not need 'dagging', having soiled wool clipped away, in a few weeks' time. Nor must the shearer leave half an inch at the end of a blow, and clean it off next time. That is double cutting, one of the worst of shearing faults, for it reduces staple length and therefore the number of uses to which the wool can be put.

Skin cuts are to be avoided if possible. In theory the modern power head will shear a sheep without marking it, but in the speed competitions especially a few cuts are invariably inflicted. Judges are most severe on wounds that the sheep can reach with its mouth, and which tend to be kept open and not allowed to heal. Infection then sets in. Loose skin behind the shoulder is easily cut, as is the flank, and these are places within reach of the sheep's teeth.

Correct holding of the sheep does much to prevent nicking. When shearing the hind leg in the Bowen method, the clenched fist is pushed hard into the lisk, where flank and hind leg meet. This has the effect of keeping that hind leg rigid and the skin over it taut. Of all the benefits of the Bowen method, the teaching of correct ways to hold the sheep for the different blows is probably the greatest.

When shearing the neck, the head is swayed over to tighten the skin. On the hindquarters, curving the body has the same effect. The worst sin is to clip a teat on a breeding ewe, but anyone careless enough for that is scarcely likely to enter a competition. The skin below the foreleg is also easily cut, and holding the leg out with the spare hand helps prevent an accident. When shearing the belly, the skin should be tautened by holding it above each blow with the foreleg tucked behind knee or elbow. It is easy to spoil a good job by carelessness in completing the tail, especially in a long-tailed sheep. The full face of the cutter head should be brought into play, for there is a danger of running its edge into the side of the tail.

Youatt in 1852 summed up the dangers of careless work:

> During the whole process of shearing the operator should anxiously avoid wounding or pricking the animal with the edge or point of the shears; otherwise the flies, abounding in the sultry heats of summer, will instantly attack the sheep, and often sting them almost to madness.

Type of sheep

A shearer must shear whatever type of sheep is set in front of him, so there is little point in discussing the various breeds. For sweet and easy shearing, however, there is nothing to touch a cross-Suffolk. Big sheep like the Suffolk/Scottish Halfbred are good to shear, as the wool peels away beautifully, and such sheep are usually kept on good land and are in fit condition. They present large areas of well-covered flesh to the shearer, contrasting with the little Welsh sheep or Swaledales which appear as a mass of bony protuberances. Horned sheep also complicate shearing; the horn tip can be unbelievably sharp and its owner has a knack of sticking it into a sensitive part of the human leg during shearing.

A point to be borne in mind by organisers is that shearlings are best for competition work. Not having borne lambs they are usually fit, but their great virtue is that they provide an even pen for each shearer. As ewes grow older they vary in condition, and a ewe that has suckled twins in spring and early summer has a different fleece from a barrener or geld ewe. Rams are quite unsuitable for competition work, and are seldom used.

Hand contests

In hill areas especially, classes for hand shearing are still held. These long-established tools are a part of the shepherd's stock-in-trade, brought into play regularly for dagging and clipping small patches in case of fly strike, and so on. With hand shears it is possible to adjust the amount of wool left, important in cold or high conditions.

Facilities

Competition conditions vary from a canvas sheet stretched on a grass field to the superb set-up for Golden Shears events at the Bath and West. Here the shearers work on a raised platform, enabling crowds estimated between one and two thousand to watch. Eight shearing units and eight individual pens are provided on the platform. The sheep to be shorn run into each shearer's pen via a race from a large holding pen below. After shearing, the sheep is popped into a chute and returns to another individual pen where her companions already shorn by the same competitor await the judges' assessment.

Individual pens have spring-loaded gates, so that as the shearer drags out his sheep, the gate springs back into the closed position. The effectiveness of this simple device is immediately apparent to onlookers, who may decide to fit spring-loaded gates to their own pens at home, thus fulfilling one of the main objects of showing.

Suggested procedure

Godfrey Bowen has much useful advice to offer the potential competitor. He suggests at least three sections: learners, intermediates, and open. The first two can be restricted to people who have not previously shorn above certain defined maximum tallies.

Another Bowen suggestion is automatic disqualification if:

1 On a ewe, the shearer cuts or cuts off a teat;
2 On a wether, he cuts or cuts off the pizzle;

3 He inflicts a cut on a sheep that causes bad or constant bleeding;
4 The overall finish of a sheep is not up to good standard.

As the shearers are shearing on exhibition, sheep should be as good as it is possible to procure. The best way to get them as even as possible is to take out all the very good-shearing sheep and then all the bad-shearing sheep. If sheep are to be dagged first, they should all be done, not just some of them. Bowen instanced one championship with thirty competitors, all capable of a tally of 300 sheep in a day. A mob of 800 Romneys was drafted, taking out the 200 best and the 200 worst, leaving 400 ewes clipping an average of $9\frac{1}{2}$lb (4.3kg) wool, and little to choose between them.

Competitors should draw for stands. They should be allowed one spare handpiece, to be used only in case of breakdowns. No time allowance can be made for stoppages or hold-ups due to faulty gear, but a fault in the shearing plant other than the handpiece should be allowed for. If a sheep escapes on the board that is also the shearer's responsibility.

Every shearer must switch off his handpiece on completing each sheep, catch his own sheep unaided, and without assistance put the shorn sheep through the porthole opening. All sheep should be tipped up after shearing, either by the judge or his assistant, to check that no rough work is hidden.

Bowen suggests a maximum of 100 points in Open Championship competitions, made up as follows:

Time	50 points
Second cuts	20 points
Finished job	30 points

Time Fastest time gains 50 points (maximum); one point is lost for every 10 seconds slower than the fastest time. If the fastest time is 5 minutes and receives 50 points, then a shearer on $5\frac{1}{2}$ minutes receives 47 points.

Second cuts One point is lost for every obvious bad patch of second cuts. The three main places where a shearer is apt to make second cuts are on the off leg and over the tail; at the start of the long blow; and the long blow itself. A few second cuts are frequently made when opening up the neck.

Bowen's ten points

No advice to a shearer can beat Godfrey Bowen's, whether in competition or on the farm. His fundamental rules are:

1 Concentrate on holding the sheep correctly.
2 Study position, and shear every place in the correct position of the sheep in relation to the machine.
3 Watch style, aiming at a steady controlled forward motion with a fast recovery. By not waving the handpiece about in the air, but bringing it back near the skin, it is made to cut wool and not air.
4 This style will allow you to concentrate on filling your comb. Shearing to a set style and pattern is a further help.
5 Try to keep on the sheep or the skin, especially with the bottom tooth of the comb. This helps eliminate second cuts.
6 Watch physical effort. Try to do the job in a way that makes shearing every part of the sheep physically easy. Shearing one sheep should be a pleasure.
7 Young shearers should not worry about speed until they have completely mastered shearing. All the top men took some time to reach their position.
8 Shear with the right balance and in a relaxed flexible style. The shearing arm should not be stiff, the wrist should be supple and the handpiece held in a light grip. A tight grip will stiffen the whole arm.
9 No one is too old to learn; listen to the advice of a clean experienced shearer.
10 Never lose your temper and fight sheep. Remember there is a fresh sheep waiting in the pen, and it is like a wrestler taking on a fresh man every round for a 200-round fight. Quality of work is paramount and is the essential qualification of a shearer.

9 Pigs

Preliminaries

Live-pig showing is governed largely by standard classes laid down by the National Pig Breeders' Association and the British Landrace Pig Society. Basically there are four male classes and four female classes, each headed by Old Boar and Old Sow and graduating through various age-brackets. This schedule is the experienced pigman's starting point. Until he knows the range of classes at a certain show on a certain date, he cannot begin to think about his entries.

Next step is to note the judges! No two are the same, and one judge won't look at the type of pig that another favours. It is a waste of time to enter pigs of the sort disliked by the judge of the class you have in mind.

Then the matings for next year's shows follow, choosing the boar and sows that you can reasonably anticipate will breed the desired type of pig. Having bred a good litter or two, it is no use picking out the best pig and leaving it at that. For a series of summer shows, a minimum of six gilts and six boars is needed. Then earmarks must be noted and entries made. Once this is done you cannot change, so those first decisions must be the right ones, with plenty of spare pigs entered to allow for things going wrong. Females are easier to breed for showing than males, for apart from getting them in-pig there is not so much scope for misfortune.

The same pig cannot win the early summer shows and be expected to be in peak form for August and September events. Similarly for the Royal; one airing at a June county show should suffice as preparation. Constant travelling and change of quarters take the edge off any pig's condition.

Stage of pregnancy

An in-pig sow or gilt is best shown half to three-quarters of the way through pregnancy. If such a sow is intended for the Royal in early July, she should farrow in February. Then, with six or eight weeks' weaning followed by service, she will farrow again in late July or early August—just right not only for the in-pig Royal Show classes, but to breed a lightweight for Smithfield in early December. Some classes specify that a gilt must have had a litter within so many weeks of the show.

In the breeding classes, females should have fourteen functional teats, and show signs of longevity potential in conformation, and especially in sound legs. Some of those early Landrace importations had sickle hocks—the selectors were evidently not horsemen, or they would never have been brought over here. The same basic principles of soundness apply to all classes of stock.

Feeding

Having made the selection, remember the old adage: 'Half the pedigree goes in at the mouth.' A skilled feeder can improve a bad pig, an unskilled one spoil a good animal. Some successful exhibitors believe in the 'wet and warm' theory. By feeding a warm mash well soaked, they aver that the pig requires less energy to heat the food to body temperature, and that it is half digested by soaking. Whether this can be proved scientifically is still open to question, but there can be no doubt about the success of these people's stock in the show-ring.

The feeder's knowledge and observation of each pig now comes into play. The commercial pig man feeds the batch, knowing that a few will do better than the average, and a few worse. The show man must get the very best from each individual, and is working to such fine margins that a quantity and diet ideal for one animal would suffice to put its litter mate off its legs.

Sheeting down a Suffolk tup. This specimen from the Malton flock carries its own advertisement on its back as well as keeping itself clean. Unsheeted stock tend to rub themselves and undo hours of work. Sheep, like other stock, become quiet through frequent and kind handling

Helicopter view of the East of England showground. The main ring has semi-circular ends, while behind it is a space for horse and gymnastic events. Left foreground is the dog show, members' facilities are in the group of white buildings right of centre, with trade stands up the left-hand side *(East of England Agricultural Society)*

Another side that the crowds don't see: early morning exercise for these Friesians, whose herdsmen have already cleaned the stalls ready for collection by the show staff. 'All stalls must be cleaned by 6am' is a common notice at major events

Mr P D Sapsed judging Herefords at the Royal Welsh, a major show with a real country flavour set in a circle of hills

Exercise

Exercise is the biggest factor here. 'Put it on and walk it off' is the show man's adage, and show pigs must be walked once and preferably twice a day. Their daily walks not only tone up muscle but accustom them to being driven and to respect and even to like human company. The pig that dislikes humans will not alter when it comes in front of a man in a bowler hat! A well-exercised pig builds muscle which enables it to stand properly. If it is a bundle of fat, it will never stand and show itself to best advantage. For training purposes it is easier if show pigs are housed separately from the rest. The pigs must become accustomed to following their herdsman around, being tempted by pieces of apple and other titbits. They must also become accustomed to the board and walking stick used to control them at summer shows. But at Smithfield they walk free, and come up to their handler without being driven.

No judge will consider a pig or any other animal that he can't approach. This quietening process is thus very important, and it is worthwhile wearing gloves for the practice sessions, as pigs have very sharp teeth. A small run with bright lights accustoms pigs to the judging ring.

Cleanliness

All this time the pigs must be kept clean. Where practical, an admirable method is to let the pigs out from their sty first thing in the morning, and allow them to dung in the yard. They soon learn and tend to retain their dung till allowed out, being naturally clean animals. Irregular timekeeping defeats the whole object, but punctuality is the hallmark of the successful exhibitor of any class of stock. If such dedication is irksome, don't try showing. Only those who feel themselves married to the job can hope to succeed. Even the best exhibitors can all recall occasions when they relaxed and missed a feed or an exercise, spoiling months of preparation in a few hours' carelessness. One lot of pigs was fed outside in round tin troughs which were removed after each feed. On one occasion the pig man did not bother, a show animal stepped on the rim of a trough, lamed itself, and was out of action for the next show.

Grooming and washing

Regarding grooming and show preparation, pigs benefit from regular oiling. Any vegetable oil—sunflower, peanut, almond or others—is preferable to the so-called pig oils that are paraffin-based. 'A pig's skin is just like a woman's—soft as silk!' claimed one enthusiast, who stressed that if you don't really love showing, far better leave it and try another walk of life.

Flowers of sulphur is a useful weapon in the show man's armoury. A tin with nail holes puncturing the lid is best for administering, and care should be taken to dress the insides of the legs and up into the crutch, the same applying to oiling. The ears must receive special treatment from the sulphur shaker, as by its use grease and canker are removed.

A week before its first show, the pig should be washed. Warm water is essential to remove all the oils and dirt in one fell swoop. Soft soap is used, and the pig cleaned thoroughly all over, not just along the back. Inside the legs and the underbelly are equally important.

After washing, wood flour is sprinkled over the white parts of the animal. Plenty should be used, and again it is vital not to miss any of the more inaccessible parts. Oils but not wood flour are applied on black or coloured parts.

Travelling

When preparing for the great day, try to arrange travel either during the night or early morning. Motorways make the modern show man's life much easier than his grandfather's, who had to load pigs on to trains, and off again at the far end, taking several days over quite a short show.

Pigs travel better when hungry. If the start is at 5 am give a last feed at 9 pm, allowing the animals time to empty themselves before being loaded. Bags packed with straw are ideal to put round the lorry sides and partitions, to prevent pigs chafing and dirtying themselves.

Once carefully loaded, the pigs' period of maximum risk is but beginning. Every year we hear horrific stories of a waggon ramp being lowered in a showground somewhere, and dead pigs tumbling out. This is simply because the driver doesn't stop periodically to see that all is well. Show pigs are in higher condition than normal slaughter pigs, and require that much extra care and supervision.

Equipment

Beginners tend to overlook the numerous articles needed on show day. The list includes a gas cylinder and copper, both for making tea and providing warm water for washing the pigs. Other essentials are: buckets, scrubbing brush, soap, show boards and sticks, grooming oil and ample feed. The veterinary and entry papers and showground passes must not be forgotten. Then there are items for the pens: nails, hammer, pincers, screwdriver for running repairs, and pitchfork, shovel, four-pronged muckfork, broom, and bedding of clean wheat straw. Lengths of sacking to fix to the pen walls are a boon if you find that the previous occupant was a black pig liberally oiled! Sacking prevents pigs scrubbing themselves against creosoted sides.

A small, neat ring in one nostril effectively prevents pigs from rooting, as they will surely do if their new pen is on fresh pasture. They will delight in throwing turf and soil all over themselves, undoing all your careful preparations in two minutes.

On the ground

At the showground, give the pigs a couple of hours to settle down before feeding. They are usually less affected than are cattle, which may refuse to drink at first. Great care is taken with the final wash. Cotton wool in the pig's ears prevents water running in. If it does, the pig will walk round the ring with its head on one side and the exhibitor will wish he had stayed at home. Washing starts at the tail, running the bucket of water forward towards the head, and *not* by throwing water into the pig's face. Parts under the tail and up between the legs must receive their share of attention. Careful drying with wood flour on the white parts follows, with oils on any coloured parts.

Driving

Boars are directed by a light square board with a hand grip cut out. Various feed firms supply these as walking adverts. A flat stick usually suffices for females, but never be tempted to use a round stick, which quickly leaves an unsightly weal on a pig's tender side.

Pigs should by now be thoroughly accustomed to walking steadily. Classes are won and lost by home schooling, not by last-minute feats of stockmanship. The best handlers ensure that the pigs walk in *front* of them, always striding out and showing to best advantage. A pig may need tapping under its head from time to time to keep that part up; no animal walks properly with its head down. A tap just behind the pig's shoulder encourages the animal to stretch out. Where pairs are shown, they must respond to the handler's voice and titbits, which again follows home schooling. If pigs don't behave at home, they most certainly won't in the ring.

NPBA

The National Pig Breeders' Association does not issue general instructions regarding showing to either agricultural societies or breeders, but does make certain conditions when classes are made for pedigree pigs and prize money provided. Each Breed Council agrees its own panel of official judges, and no prize support is given to a society unless it appoints a judge from that panel. Panels are reviewed every year, to ensure that judges listed are still active and fully aware of current trends within the breed.

Detailed information relating to each pig shown must be

printed in the catalogue, stipulates the NPBA. First comes the ear number and registered name, and the Herd Book number, or volume in which the animal is entered. Prizes may be withheld if this ear number and name are missing from the catalogue. The number of pigs born alive and the number alive at three weeks in the litter from which the entry is drawn must also be given, together with date of birth of the entry, and names and Herd Book numbers of sire and dam. Where the breeder is not the exhibitor, the breeder's name must be printed in the catalogue.

All female pigs (except Large White) born before 1 January shall be eligible to compete only if in the six months before the show they have farrowed, suckled and reared a litter to three weeks, or have done so after 1 January. In the case of Large Whites, females born before 1 July of the previous year shall have either produced a litter in the year of the show, or produced a live litter within twelve weeks of the first day of the show.

Boars of two years of age and over (all breeds) are to be certified as having sired at least three live litters within the twelve months preceding the date on which entries close. Boars aged eighteen months and more at the time of showing must have their tusks cut before going to a show.

The use of artificial colouring, whitening and powder on pigs as well as the removal or addition of spots by artificial means is prohibited. The last restriction does not apply to Large Whites.

The NPBA Standards of Excellence follow.

Large White

Head Moderately long, face slightly dished, snout broad, not too much turned up, jowl light, wide between the ears
Ears Long, thin, slightly forward, and fringed with hair
Neck Clean, medium length and proportionately full to shoulders
Shoulders Medium to good width, free from coarseness and not too deep

Back, Loin and Ribs Long with slightly arched back and wide from neck to rump; ribs well sprung to allow good muscling; free from weakness behind shoulder and loin

Hams Broad, well muscled at the side and back and deep to hocks; ample length from pin bone to tail

Tail Well set and strong

Underline Fourteen sound, well-spaced teats, free from supernumeraries; with boars at least three on each side in front of the sheath

Legs Straight and set well apart with plenty of bone

Pasterns Short, strong and springy

Feet Strong with even cleys

Action Firm and free

Skin Fine, white, free from wrinkles and black and blue spots

Coat Silky and free from roses

The Standard of Excellence has been designed in the light of known requirements of the meat and breeding trades bearing in mind the avoidance of excessive fat. All efforts to appraise the relative merits of pigs shall be made against a background of the killing-out value of the animal at the correct weight and age. The failure of an animal to reach the Standard of Excellence in some breed characteristics shall not outweigh its obvious value from a carcass point of view. (Revised 1975)

Welsh

Head Light, fine and fairly wide between the ears which should tend to meet at the tips short of the nose

Nose Straight and clean jowl

Neck Clean and not too deep

Shoulders Light, but with forelegs set well apart, somewhat flat topped and shoulder leading into really well sprung ribs. Lack of depth down through the shoulders and chest is most important

Back Long, strong and level with well-sprung ribs giving a fairly wide mid-back and dropping slightly to the tail which should be thick and free from depressions at root

Loin Well muscled, firm and well developed, the belly and

flank to be thick, the underline straight

Hindquarters Strong with hams full, firm and thick, whether viewed from back or sides and full to hocks but not flabby

Legs The pig should not appear leggy, and the legs should be straight and set well apart with short pasterns and good strong bone

Coat Straight and fine; roses and crown back are undesirable.

Skin Fine and free from wrinkles

Teats Evenly placed and number at least twelve in both boars and females

Colour White; blue spots undesirable

Action Pigs should be active, alert and move freely and easily

British Saddleback

Colour Black and white but with a continuous belt of white hair encircling the shoulders and forelegs

Head Medium length, face very slightly dished, under-jaw clean-cut and free from jowl; medium width between ears

Ears Medium size, carried forward, curbing but not obscuring vision

Neck Clean and of medium length

Shoulders Medium width, free from coarseness, not too deep

Chest Wide and not too deep

Back Long and straight

Loin Broad and strong, free from slackness

Ribs Well sprung

Sides Long and medium depth

Hams Broad, full and well filled to hocks

Underline Straight and with at least twelve well-placed teats

Legs Strong with good bone, straight, well set on each corner of the body

Feet Strong and of good size

Coat Fine, silky and straight

Action Firm and free

Disqualification: an animal not possessing a continuous band of white hair over the shoulders and forelegs is ineligible for registration in the Herd Book.

Objectionable features:
Head Badger face, short or turned-up snout
Ears Pricked or floppy
Hair Curly or coarse coat, coarse mane, rose on back or
    shoulder
Skin Coarse or wrinkled, chocolate coloured
Teats Unsound or unevenly placed teats
(Revised 1971)

Finished pigs

The various weight ranges are fundamental to showing finished
pigs. A typical range is:

Porker	110–136lb (50–62kg)
Cutter	150–176lb (68–80kg)
Baconer	187–209 lb (85–95 kg)
Heavy pig	231–264lb (105–120kg)

All these weights are liveweight. If the pigs are too young, they
will not make the weight. If too old, they must be held back,
and this takes off the bloom. The average liveweight gain per
day at the different stages of growth in your own herd must be
known, and related to date of birth and thus to serving date.

The same type of pig will not do for all the various classes, so
the skilled pig man must known what type of litter a sow
throws. Smithfield Show falls in early December, and heavy
pigs need six months to be ready. This entails farrowing early
in June. For bacon classes, the first week in July is all right,
while the Smithfield cutter will not be born until late July, and
the porker in mid-August.

Showing pigs is part of commercial pig keeping. It is done to
make a name for the breeder. Therefore normal commercial
practice should be followed as far as possible. For instance,
you may have a specially good sow that throws just the right
sort of piglets to make the Smithfield bacon classes. Though
she may be held back for service three weeks beyond her
normal time to fit in, it would be quite unacceptable to hold her
back longer.

In the live/dead classes, the usual procedure is a pen of three, of which one pig goes to kill. The three are first judged alive to a given points scale, and the judge's job is to estimate what each pig would look like on the hook. He conjures in his mind the various points. Length from behind the shoulder to the pin bone is sought, as are full hams, spring of rib and well-made loins. The butcher, and therefore the judge, seeks a flat shoulder that does not carry any fat. Teats and legs are not important at this stage: the pig's walking days are done, its breeding prospects are nil.

A heavy head on the pig is not wanted, nor is a thick jowl. Neither brain nor brawn is a favourite dish today, so there is no point in providing the raw materials. The Danes have consistently bred pigs with smaller and smaller heads. It is pointless to have cheap cuts forming more of the carcass than absolutely necessary. The money lies between the shoulders and the tail head. A show pig ought not to be too thick at the poll; its back should be firm to the touch, not flabby; its tail lean. These points indicate carcass quality throughout.

Though Landrace, Large White and Welsh predominate in the carcass classes, there are some neat pigs among the Hampshires. British Saddlebacks tend to be used more as foundation dams in crossing programmes. To the general public, the finer points of a bacon pig are less obvious than on a prize steer, but differences become more apparent if the points mentioned are studied and the herdsmen asked to illustrate the variations.

A typical Smithfield range in this section is:

Porkers Each weighing 110–136lb (50–62kg) liveweight, born on or after 1 August
Cutters Each weighing 150–176lb (68–80kg) liveweight, born on or after 1 July
Baconers Each weighing 187–209lb (85–95kg) liveweight, born on or after 1 June

The Royal Show stages classes for the widest range of breeds. Large White, Landrace, Middle White, Tamworth,

Berkshire, British Saddleback, Large Black, Welsh, Gloucestershire Old Spot and Hampshire are all included. British Lops and Gloucestershire Old Spots are also shown at the Bath and West, while the Great Yorkshire stages groups of pigs by the same boar. The East of England's pig classes include a Bacon Carcass Competition run in accordance with the recommendations of the National Advisory Committee for Pig Carcass Competition.

YFC pig judging

Young Farmers' Club pig-judging competitions are popular events, and at Smithfield there are two rings of live pigs, the same pigs being brought back later as carcasses. One ring is of four Landrace, 160–220lb (72–99kg) liveweight; the other is of four cross-bred White pigs in the 120–150lb (54–67kg) range.

Each competitor judges one ring of live pigs and carcasses, afterwards giving observations on the live animals and reasons on the carcasses. The scale of points to be followed is:

Inspection

Proportion of lean to fat	20
Fullness of eye muscle	20
Shape of leg	20
Lightness of shoulder	10
Firmness and whiteness of fat	5
Colour and texture of flesh	5
Neat and small head	5
	85

Measurement

Length for weight	15
	100

Scale of marking

Observations—10 marks for each animal for its potential as a carcass	40
Style	10
	50
Carcass: Placing	50
Reasons:	
Accuracy of observations	25
Comparison	15
Style	10
	50
Total per competitor	150
Total per team	300

10 Goats

Dairy-cow breeders are frequently astonished at the modern goat's milking potential. As a converter of animal into human food on a liveweight comparison, she is far more efficient than many a Friesian. Yet as with any high-performance animal or machine, the chances of mishap are greater, and no other farm animal is so easily upset by changes of food or environment.

Special needs

Thus the goat exhibitor has special problems. Water is the first one; take a goat to a summer show and she will probably refuse all water despite the heat—that is, unless something is done about it. The simple and cheap solution is to add salt to the water at home, so that when her ladyship is at the Royal or the Bath and West, she does not notice the difference.

Though all livestock exhibitors take a first-aid kit with them, a more than usually comprehensive one is advised for goats. The packing list of one leading exhibitor includes scour mixture, bloat mixture and cider vinegar: the last is admirable for stomach upsets; tubes of terramycin and penicillin, and terramycin sprays, are needed in case udder complaints spring up suddenly. Thermometer, cottonwool, scissors, Dettol, milk of magnesia and salt are essentials. However there is always a veterinary surgeon in attendance at leading showgrounds, and some competitors prefer to rely on his stocks.

For grooming, brushes, comb, scissors, sponge and towels are required, and a bucket for washing water. Other buckets are for milking and feeding.

A hay rack or net is standard equipment, custom-built show racks being available which hook on to the hurdle cross bars, and obviate accidents that happen when a goat pokes its forefoot through a series of meshes. Hay, straw, green food and leafy branches of hazel, elm or willow complete the feed list. If kids are being shown, a steriliser for the bottle and a filter for straining milk are necessary.

A box of talcum powder, hair oil, shampoo and white blanco or chalk for knees are also listed. Collars and leads, and a headstall for a male goat should be included, though some exhibitors prefer to hang on to the beard! They reserve headstalls for male goats moved by rail. Every goat exhibitor *must* wear a white coat, and spare goat coats may be needed. The goat coat is an essential part of every stud's equipment. Goats are 'coated up' after washing, for if this is not done, winter hair curls rather than lies flat.

Shampoos

The best shampoo to use causes some divergence of opinion among lady-goat owners, with human, cattle and horse shampoos all having their adherents. A dual-purpose shampoo that cleans hands, face or hair has the advantage of producing few suds and requiring no pre-soaking. It may be put on neat and left for half an hour on badly stained patches. The first washing is done a month before the show, one objective being to get rid of the winter coat.

For these pre-show washings, warm water is preferred whatever the season. The animal must be thoroughly wet all over, but the cattle herdsman's trick of using a hose-pipe does not find favour among goat owners. Working in the shampoo thoroughly and then rinsing it out, usually suffices. Any bad stains are given separate treatment.

Trimming

Trimming fashions vary. Most exhibitors do not trim a male goat's mane, but a female looks younger with the beard shaved. Long hairs between the front legs are also trimmed. A goat at kidding inevitably discharges on to her tail and daily washing is advised. If the stained hairs are trimmed at kidding, they will grow again before the show season.

Feet should be scrubbed clean, and horns scrubbed and

oiled. Horned goats are not generally shown, however; there is too much risk of them damaging their fellows in the transport. Care of the feet is a year-round business, and excess growth must be trimmed regularly. It is of no use discovering a few days before the first show that a favoured animal has curly, overgrown hoofs.

Travel

Goats, like other stock, travel best on empty stomachs. A van or trailer is used, and the universal stock rule must be repeated: don't trust to luck once the animals are loaded, but stop and inspect at regular intervals.

On arrival at the showground, contact the class stewards. They will check the necessary number cards, and give directions to the pens. Unloading is done without further delay, and the goats left with a rackful of hay to munch if they wish, and half an hour in which to settle down.

Milking and inspection classes

In milking classes, action starts on the evening of arrival. At a time stated on the schedule, usually early evening, the goats are milked out. This is not a haphazard event, but is done to time in the gangway under supervision of the stewards. Udders are checked and stripped out by the stewards. Being late for stripping does not disqualify the entrant, but it means that the goat has less time in which to produce milk for the vital morning weighing, so a latecomer penalises himself.

After stripping out, the exhibitors see to their own evening meal. The goats are fed, so that the interval till morning is not too long, and the rest of the evening is spent according to inclination, which for most showing people means a chat with fellow competitors about their particular stock. Last thing before bed, the goats are again inspected, sheets round the pens checked for draught-proofing, clean water given if necessary.

An early start is needed next morning as the first inspection is around 7 am. To rise at 5.30 or 6 am is the general rule, the first thoughts being for the goats. Having checked that all is well, a quick cup of tea is called for, and then the goat is prepared for the ring at 7 am. This first appearance before the judges is done with full udders. The animals are placed with their rear ends to the judge under the stewards' directions. At this stage only the udders are examined. Then the goats are turned sideways, walked round and out of the ring. White overalls are essential.

Then the all-important first milking takes place in the alleyways, *never* in the pens. Buckets are tipped upside-down, to prove that no extra pints are added to the day's tally, and after milking their own charges by hand the exhibitors take their buckets to the weighing steward, who samples the milk for butterfat testing.

Breakfast follows, then preparations are made for the inspection classes starting at 9 am. The judge has records of kidding dates, and the amount of milk given. Conformation, skin texture, eyes, absence of lumps and all the other points which make up the perfect goat are considered. Exhibitors are asked to walk their charges first in one direction, then in the other. The line-up is made, and further examination undertaken. Breed points are important here; Anglo-Nubians must have long ears, Saanens may be smaller than British Saanens.

The second milking takes place some twelve hours after the first, the procedure of gangway milking being repeated, and weighings and samples carried out as before. At this stage, all placings are known except the yield results. No one is allowed to leave the milking arena until all have finished, although kids and goatlings may be allowed to leave before the completion of milking classes.

Unlike cows, goats usually receive their concentrate ration *after* milking. They are milked while cudding, letting down their milk better than if they are feeding.

Training goats for the ring starts when they are a month old. A small collar is used, and though no animal may be shown before it is two calendar months old, these early lessons in leading are invaluable. In the ring, goats show themselves best if allowed to walk naturally.

A goat may be taught to stand correctly at home. To 'set it up', ready for the judge's eye, entails placing the front legs straight down, the rear ones slightly outwards, and the head slightly up. The object is to present a straight topline. If front and hind legs are too far apart, the back will dip; if too close, it will arch.

Goatlings tend to improve during the show season. They are growing all the time, and becoming more accustomed to the show atmosphere and being away from home.

A thick, heavy collar should never be used on a show goat. A slender, neat and clean piece of leather helps give the impression of length in the neck, while a thick band does the opposite. There is much to be said for plaited, washable show leads.

Immediately before entry to the ring, blanco or chalk is applied to the animals' knees if they are stained. The chalk comes in blocks as supplied by dog requisite shops. A dark goat receives different treatment from a white one, washing being the sole preparation for coloured animals.

Kidding

March is the favourite month for show goats to kid. In any event, they must kid down at least ten days before the first milking trials of the season to be eligible for entry. These trials usually begin early in May, so the five-month gestation period must allow for this. The March date has an added advantage in that kids are likely to have completed their required two calendar months of age to become eligible for entry.

If an animal fails to produce kids by the age of two years, she is ineligible to compete in recognised shows. All shows 'recognised' by the British Goat Society have to be held under BGS rules. Ages: kids, two to twelve months; goatlings, twelve to twenty-four months, *not* having borne a kid; milkers, must have borne a kid at least ten days before the show-day milking trials. All championship and breed championship awards have to be ratified by a minimum points score in the milking trials.

The art of feeding a milker is to keep her in good condition

Before . . . Clydesdales at the Glasgow Stallion Show, held in spring before the weather warms up. Quality of feather on the legs is an important show point in Clydesdales and Shires. These youngsters do not receive the decorations bestowed on older horses

And after . . . a smile and a model Suffolk from Her Majesty Queen Elizabeth the Queen Mother for Marshland Bette and her owner. Heavy horses are one of the great attractions of the modern show-ring, even more than when they were seen on the streets every day *(East of England Agricultural Society)*

A busy scene as the Golden Shears contest is staged at the Royal Bath and West. Each shearer is scrutinised by an experienced judge. Throughout the match the judges move to different competitors. Wrapping proceeds in the foreground *(Royal Bath and West)*

The Swaledale 'Royal' at England's highest pub, Tan Hill, 1,732ft above sea level. Sited on an old drovers' road in the middle of miles of moorland, this event is noted for cold weather but that does not deter spectators who come from far afield

during pregnancy. She must never lose weight at this time, for once she comes into milk it is most difficult to combine show condition with high milk yield, and some liveweight loss is inevitable.

Matings are arranged to correct faults or deficiencies. A 'cow-hocked' female is mated to a male of very sound legs, a heavy-shouldered female to a male with the opposite tendencies, while undue slope to the tail or a dip along the topline are conformation faults which breeders try to improve by corrective matings. Udder shape and texture, milk yield and body size are other vital points.

11 Heavy Horses

Those wishing to join the boom in heavy horse showing face stiff competition, for there are no keener stock exhibitors in the country. This should be a spur rather than a deterrent for there is ample room in the ranks, and showing opportunities spread year by year as more and more societies add or restore the heavy to their schedules. Certainly there is no greater crowd-puller, and sponsorships are being offered to counter the high cost of transporting a heavy horse.

Britain has four breeds of heavy horses: Clydesdale, Percheron, Shire and Suffolk. The Shires are the most numerous and probably the most expensive, the rewards being commensurately greater if a tip-top animal is brought out. North of the Border the Clydesdale predominates, while both Percherons and Suffolks hold sway in the eastern counties.

Apart from in-hand classes, heavy-horse enthusiasts have the chance to enter turn-outs (two- or four-wheeled vehicles), decorated horses and plough teams. Membership of a breed society and heavy horse associations helps.

The new entry cannot get away from the old saying 'No foot, no horse.' A horse's feet must be looked after with care, all through its life. So rule number one is to buy a horse with sound feet, and not be misled into thinking that sadly neglected hoofs can be restored to top condition by a short course of treatment.

The potential show animal must have correct breed and conformation points; unless the main desirable properties are there, it is no use proceeding.

Feeding

Having obtained or bred a suitable animal, feeding must be studied with care. Small, regular feeds, starting at least two months before show date, are called for. This does not mean that a lot of corn is needed; quality hay is the basic winter requirement. Any foal you have bred or hope to buy should be eating hard food from the trough well before weaning. Nor is too early weaning desirable. A regular worming routine should be carried out, frequency and amounts varying with the age of the animal, but by following the schedule of a reputable firm of drug manufacturers, these parasites can be controlled.

Hair and grooming

Hair and 'feather'—the long hair on the fetlocks of Shires and Clydesdales, but largely absent from Suffolks and Percherons—should be dressed regularly with a light oil to which a handful of flowers of sulphur has been added. Some horsemen recommend pig oil. When applying the oil, always stroke the hair downwards, rubbing into the roots of the hair, the way the hair is hanging. Hoofs should be dressed with hoof oil twice a month, and watched for even growth. The blacksmith may have to be called in to ensure sound feet.

Grooming depends on the time of year, and whether the horse sleeps under a roof or not. Stock lying at pasture, whether in summer or winter, should not be groomed as the dust and the natural oils and sweat in the coat act as a protective.

If inside, horses should be groomed with curry comb and dandy brush, the main function of the curry comb being to clean the brush. This conventional 'strapping' is done to tone up the muscles. There are on the market appliances to remove the dust from the coat but, though these may be admirable for that function, the toning-up of muscles can only be done by real work on them. The horse should be groomed by starting at the head and working systematically over the whole animal, following identical procedures on each occasion.

Even if your horse is lying out, tail and mane may receive attention. A strong mane comb is needed, for neglected manes take many groomings and a lot of work before they hang nicely on one side of the animal. Let us hope that the fashion of hogged or close-clipped manes on heavies never takes root in Britain.

The tail needs equal care. If it has remained uncombed for two or three years, a blunt penknife drawn downwards through the hair reduces the tangle. Then it must be worked a bit at a time until the mane comb can be drawn through it at any point.

Leading and standing

A show horse must be taught to lead, and walk and trot with its groom. The best time to put a halter on is within twenty-four hours of birth, but this counsel of perfection may not have been practised on a bought-in animal. Birth is often the best time to assess the future leg development of the youngster. If a foal has a small halter put on its head very early, and realises that it is being held, the lesson goes home for life.

With older foals, it is necessary to tie them to a post, or for a strong man to hold them firmly. When tied up, the youngster must become accustomed to handling. Run the hands all over it, starting on the nose, then the rest of the face, the ears, neck and forelegs—this should be done from either side, right down to the hind legs; then pick up each of the hoofs in turn. If a horse doesn't have its feet picked up until a strange man in an apron approaches with a piece of sizzling metal, it is hardly likely to appreciate the situation. A foal brought up to be handled quietly, kindly and regularly will rarely give trouble unless frightened or abused.

Horses should be talked to at all times. Pocock wrote: 'Only as I learned to welcome horses when they came to me, I seemed to sense their feelings. They converse among themselves by thought-transference, and try to speak that way to men they trust.' That trust comes only through constant association, consistently kind treatment and regular talking.

When teaching a horse to walk and trot, the lesson should take place alongside a solid wall or fence. It is no use if the animal can swing away from its groom to avoid chastisement. The whip is carried for guidance more than anything else, but schooling is done at home, not in the show-ring.

Whenever an in-hand horse is pulled up, he should be made to stand correctly. Weight should be evenly balanced over all four legs, which should be properly spaced and not set at awkward angles. If this trait is cultivated from an early age, the horse soon falls into line and automatically halts to best advantage.

Shoeing

As the show date approaches, legs, mane and tail should be washed weekly. Ten days before, a visit to the smith is necessary. A skilled smith can help correct small defects in a horse's action by suitable shoeing. Horses are occasionally 'pricked' by a shoe nail and go lame, hence the ten days allowed for shoeing before the show. A very strong coronet head is necessary on a show horse—or any other, for that matter. A narrow, donkey-like joint is no use, and the hoof must be sound and bold, rather than shelly.

If judging is not early in the day and the show is near home, the horse is loaded into his transport on the morning of the show. Otherwise an overnight stop is necessary. Washing the day before and a quiet entry into the waggon are both necessary. On arrival a light feed and a bucket of water are offered, after which begins the business of plaiting up.

Braiding

A braid or bass may be bought, consisting of three ribbons and raffia. There are a few basic rules to help an art in which much practice is needed to achieve perfection:

1 The mane should be slightly dampened.
2 Plaiting should start as close to the poll as possible. A plait starting several inches down the neck never compares with one begun high.
3 Ensure that the horse's head remains erect during plaiting. The decorations will then be at the correct angle.
4 Plait tightly—a slack plait is never impressive.
5 Continue plaiting almost to the withers. A plait that ends halfway down the neck looks bad.

The mane is first brushed down the offside of the horse's neck. Only small bunches of hair are used to plait the braid into the mane. An upright is inserted at regular intervals, using from nine to fourteen per animal according to size and the whim of the decorator.

When plaiting a Shire's tail, the bob or bun must be set as high as possible. This may be helped by plaiting in small bits of raffia, with a few pieces of hair left to cover the dock. Tail plaiting has altered completely since the anti-docking laws. The hair of the tail is divided into three to plait, leaving aside some hairs to hang down. In some cases, including Suffolks, horses are shown with long tails, in which case washing is the most important part of the operation, and the hair is brushed till it hangs quite freely.

Headgear

Stallions of two years and upwards must be shown in a roller and crouper, bit and bearing rein. This outfit must be clean, smart and correctly fitted, and the stallion thoroughly accustomed to its use before show day. Seldom does a heavy-breed stallion play up these days. In the Percheron world especially, stallions are harnessed in mixed teams.

For mares, younger females and geldings, a clean white halter is best. The groom should always be appropriately turned out and smart. 'Never let down the animal being shown' is a personal rule for all classes of stock.

In the ring

The stewards will call for horses to be led from their loose boxes to the collecting ring, if there is one, at the appropriate time. At all times co-operate with and obey the stewards. On entering the ring, the practice at most shows is to walk clockwise, but Shire men at the East of England Showground proceed anti-clockwise, moving straight across the ground and turning left-handed to pass close to the grandstand on their right. Walk round at a steady pace, giving the animal in front several yards' clearance. Crowded stock do not show themselves to full advantage.

After the judge has watched this encircling walk to his satisfaction, he calls the class into his preliminary order, usually standing them from right to left as he faces them. He then examines each animal individually, or should do.

An experienced horse judge gave a few simple rules for competitors at this point:

1 Wait for the judge's inspection, holding the animal to full advantage throughout.
2 Wait for the judge to speak.
3 When he does, be polite and co-operative. His only greeting may well be 'Good morning', to which the only appropriate reply is 'Good morning, sir'.
4 Answer any questions to the best of your ability. Usually there are none, but in a mixed class the judge may well ask the age of your animal.
5 Do *not* try to enter into a conversation with the judge!

The next stage is a request from the judge to show the animal. Each competitor awaits his turn, and walks in a direct line away from the judge in the direction indicated. At the turn, slow down virtually to a dead stop, and turn right-handed so that the horse is between groom and judge. A left-hand turn is suspect; the handler may be trying to hide some faulty action. The same applies to too tight a hold on the horse's head. Proceed straight back towards the judge, turn, and repeat at the trot. The judge is noting the animal's action, and must be helped to do so.

Finally, a small man has an advantage when showing a big horse. The late Reg Nunn's Shires towered above him as they trotted out to perfection. It would be out of place to compare contemporary grooms, but all who saw him admitted the skill of Reg Nunn in showing great horses at their best.

Sequence of examination

There is much to be said for a system of examining animals in logical sequence. First impressions count. In the case of the horse, temperament and disposition are indicated by the expression of countenance, and the set of the ears. Then all features of the head, the width and depth of the chest, the setting, direction and conformation of the forelegs and feet are noted. Passing to the side (usually beginning with the near side), stature and scale, length or compactness, depth of flank and the carriage and shape of head and neck are considered. The eye passes to the shortness and levelness of the topline, the length and straightness of the underline, slope of the shoulders and height and shape of the withers. Forelegs and feet are then studied from side-on, then the back, rib, loin, flank, croup, tail, stifle, thigh, hind legs and feet.

From behind the hips are noted—their symmetry, width, levelness and rotundity. Fullness of thighs and quarters, and direction and conformation of hind legs and feet may be determined from this angle. Repeating the procedure from the opposite side to confirm the original side view completes this stage. The actual sequence of examination is less important than the discipline of using exactly the same method on every animal examined.

When studying the horse in action, the directness and rapidity of his stride, especially behind, may be noted as he is moved away. As he comes back, or 'meets you', the directness, rapidity and freedom of the stride in front is seen.

Boldness, courage and manners are well seen from the front and then, as the horse is led past, the spring, height, length and balance of the stride are noted, together with a general impression of the horse in action. Though an expert judge may not consciously use such a definite system, he almost certainly does so without being aware of the sequence.

The general points to consider in judging any horses, including heavies, may be summarised:

1 General appearance—height, weight, style, symmetry, colour and markings
2 Form—setting on legs, width, depth, compactness, contour
3 Conformation
4 Quality—hide and hair, bone, finish, general refinement
5 Substance—proportion of weight to height; bone and muscling
6 Constitution—chest and abdominal capacity; evidence of thrift and vigour
7 Condition—degree of fatness; fitness for work
8 Way of going
9 Age—determination, significance
10 Soundness
11 Temperament and disposition

Soundness

The definition of soundness is that there be no partial or total loss of function which prevents a horse from performing the ordinary duties of his class. Most unsoundnesses have their origin in structural defects or imperfections. Side bones are most common on the outer quarters of wide-fronted draft horses, such horses tending to be 'pigeon-toed', and this brings the outer quarter nearer to the centre of weight-bearing, causing weight and wear which should be borne by the other quarter. The result is ossification of the cartilage. Such an unsoundness may render the animal useless, yet there are other forms of unsoundness which have little effect on the work for which the animal is used. Unsoundness causing little or no inconvenience, and not liable to, is of only slight consequence to the buyer.

Disposition

Whether for work, sport or show, a horse of cheerfully responsive disposition is a tremendous asset. Coupled with intelligence, it determines an animal's usefulness within the limits of its capabilities as fixed by type, conformation and soundness. We have all met good, honest, game horses that give far better service despite some physical disability than a sound yet crabbed, sour or stupid animal.

The best show, riding or work horses enter fully into the spirit of the occasion—the best-known example being Red Rum. We can't all expect to find a Red Rum, but the capable judge looks at the expression in a horse's eye, the poise and movement of its ear, and its reaction towards mankind and other horses. There is much to be learnt from keen study of a horse's head.

Decorated classes

An aspiring entrant for the many classes for heavy horse decorations will seek a standard of points to guide him. Unfortunately, none exists. The great pleasure that spectators gain from these events is not always matched by the exhibitors'. They can use only their own ideas and guess at the judges' whims, which vary considerably. Some give half the points to the horse, others aver that the harness and not the horse is being judged. Shining brasses may be set above gaily coloured flowers, while at the next show the reverse is the case. One ploughman admitted that he always included scented flowers for a particular lady judge, and always gained first prize!

Woollen decorations find favour in Scotland, ear muffs in southern England. Fly terrets may contain a number of small bells. Though it is impossible to be dogmatic about the most suitable decorations, views from qualified judges and organisers may be repeated.

From Windsor, Mr C R Hannis deems the artistic approach the best one for the judge to take:

One has to look at the turn-out through the eyes of an artist. Above all, one should look for quality and neatness, not quantity. Some exhibitors so overload the horse with a mass of brass that in extreme cases one can scarcely see the horse for the trappings. I suggest 25 per cent for the horse and 75 per cent for the decorations. Such things as different methods of plaiting tails and manes should be judged on how well they are done, not one method against another.

The Southern Counties Heavy Horse Association is to the fore in organising turn-out classes. Secretary Mrs Mary Dash says: 'There are strong regional prejudices. Our southern horsemen regard floral decorations as beyond words. Yet the variations in decorations are still wide.'

SCHHA ploughing match programmes give this guide:

In the competition for best turned out plough teams, colour and size of the horses do not affect the judging at all because, although it may look smart to have two horses of the same colour, these horses have been matched together for their ability *to work in harness as a team* and are judged with this in mind.

Every horse must however be thoroughly clean (you may see the judge run a hand over the coat for traces of grease or dust) and it must be well groomed from its head right down to its hoofs. Harness must fit correctly and be comfortable for the horse to wear, so the judges check each item to make sure that not only does it fit properly, but that the leather is clean, supple and in good order and that all buckles are sound and in good easy working order. Stiff buckles make it difficult to get harness off quickly in an emergency.

All the brass will be examined to make certain that it is thoroughly clean, both on the face and the back, and that it is all correctly fixed and in good order. The intricate plaits and braidings on manes and tails are also examined and assessed, as are the flowing manes and tails which the horsemen have from their own preference left free. Ear caps too are taken into account.

Pulling matches

A show-ring spectacle that is returning to Britain is the pulling match. Unofficial contests between heavy horses have been recorded, especially among Suffolks, the sport is strongly established in North America, and the organisers of the Soham, Cambridgeshire, Carnival have pioneered its re-introduction here.

Teams of either one or two horses pull a type of sledge, known as a stoneboat, over a distance of $27\frac{1}{2}$ feet (8.4 metres). This precise distance has been calculated as that for which a horse can exert its full power. Increased weight, usually in the form of cement blocks, is added until the team is defeated, and the last team left in the contest is the winner.

On the face of it, this seems cruel. Yet American enthusiasts (and pulling people really are enthusiasts) stress that the horses are trained up to the event in the manner of an athlete, that they thoroughly enjoy the work and excitement, and that they are really 'rarin' to go'.

Rules are very strict. No whips, no bad language, no intoxicating liquor. The horses are divided into classes by their weight, a team of two amassing less than 3,200lb (1,453kg) being considered a middleweight. Over that combined weight they are heavyweights, and the bigger teams total 4,600 or 4,700lb (2,088 or 2,133kg). A lightweight class is for horses making 2,800–3,200lb (1,271–1,452kg) the pair.

Horses are first yoked to fairly light loads to build up muscle and confidence; extra strong harness is needed, with double-strength hames and reinforced tugs.

The Belgian is the most popular breed in American pulling circles. These modern, tall American Belgians are very different from the rather squat Continental animals resembling Ardennes horses now found in Britain. The world record was set in 1971 by Fowler Brothers of Michigan, with a pull of 4,375lb (2,186kg) over the full $27\frac{1}{2}$ feet (8.4 metres). Bigger loads have been shifted, but not over the required distance.

Competitive spirit is as important in pulling horses as in any other sport. American teamster Marshall Grass said of his team Dick and Prince: 'You had to keep them as quiet as you could before a pull. They got excited just like kids. They could smell a horse pull coming and were always ready.' This pair of Belgians eats a 40lb (18kg) bale of hay between them every day. They also receive several feeds a day of a home mixture of corn, molasses, vitamins and minerals. When at home they are turned out for exercise each summer night after the flies have disappeared. Like so many stockmen the world over, Marshall Grass regards the animal's head as vital, and it is the first thing he looks for in a pulling horse. He seeks a Roman-nosed horse for his team.

Each team has three chances to pull the weight. If the team fails on the first pull, the driver may keep his team hitched and try again after one minute's rest. If the object is still not achieved, the driver can unhitch and place the load anywhere he chooses for his final try. Sometimes a team becomes so excited after failing the first pull that they are unhitched, but by doing so the driver forfeits one of his two remaining chances.

12 Judging

Every breeder and buyer of livestock must be a judge. That does not necessarily mean that he will stand bowler-hatted in a crowded ring but that he must at some time choose an animal to mate or buy. Judging is more than measuring to a standard, or the analysis of the stock under consideration. There must be comparisons leading to definite conclusions.

As one exponent of the show-ring remarked: 'It is the balancing of the sum total of merit and deficiency of one individual against that of another, after the same fashion that a judge on the bench weighs all the evidence before returning a verdict.'

Judging is selection. It is the means whereby the breeder aims at his goal of the perfect animal by mating the approved and culling the undesirable individuals. It is not merely confined to placing awards in the show-ring, though that is an important function—it establishes ideals and standards that will lead or mislead the rank and file of breeders. The successful buyer or breeder *must* be a good judge, whether or not he decides the placing of rosettes.

Attributes

The twin attributes of an outstanding judge are accuracy and rapidity. His trained eye ensures not only that he is right, but that he does not lose time. Take half a second too long, and the hammer is down. The chance has been missed. The heifer or filly that was to improve our herd has gone elsewhere because we could not make up our minds rapidly enough, and we may rue the consequences for years. This has happened to all stock people at some time, but to the top men it happens less and less frequently.

Stock pass through the sale ring at the rate of one a minute, and the person who can choose accurately and rapidly is the one who is likely to pick the cream from forty or fifty newly-calven heifers or shearling rams within the show-ring's white rails.

Correlations are recognised, sometimes intuitively. A long-legged animal tends also to be long in neck and body, but proportionately narrow and shallow bodied. A particularly wide animal may well be deep bodied and short legged. Systematic methods of observing help both accuracy and dispatch. Each look is made to count, repetitions and omissions are avoided, and while the proportions and relations of the parts are kept in mind, an all-embracing conception of the whole animal is obtained. This wholly professional way of sizing up an animal, compared with the novice approach, has never been better expressed than by Somerville and Ross in *Some Experiences of an Irish RM*:

'Bernard stared at the horse in silence; not the pregnant and intimidating silence of the connoisseur, but the tongue-tied muteness of helpless ignorance.'

Choosing judges

The judge is the kingpin in the whole edifice of showing. If he is incompetent, slack or biased, the parade becomes a charade. The last word on any topic concerning his class rests with the judge, and bad judging ruins a show more quickly than poor entries.

Selection of judges for the bigger shows begins with the breed societies. Their council draws up a list of judges, men of long experience with the class of stock concerned, and preferably with some showing experience. They must have 'an eye for an animal', be able to see what is under the skin and know the difference between real quality and show condition. To be able to 'carry an animal in the eye', to remember its points and size having once seen it, is not quite so important in the show-ring as the animals are there in front of the man in charge.

Some excellent judges are found among young people. Having grown up with Swaledale sheep or Shorthorn cattle, they may have crammed in more hours of direct work among stock than an older person coming to a breed later in life or caring for it only part-time. Younger judges tend to be more impartial—which is not meant as a slur on older ones, but as people become more involved with a breed some succumb to the temptation to place the man rather than the animal.

The appropriate breed societies are approached by show committees for lists of their approved judges. Suitable ones, who have not been asked too many times in the past, are then invited by letter. The show committee will be wise to select one judge and one reserve, hoping that one or other will accept.

The prospective judge should either accept or decline immediately. Drawing up a list of suitable officials is no light task, made harder by tardy replies to invitations. If our judge accepts, there are certain lines for him to follow between acceptance and show day.

Possibly one man is asked to judge two breeds, and is more familiar with one than the other. He must then make a point to gain knowledge of the less-known breed, but to do so without any reference whatsoever to those likely to exhibit. This is easier said than done, especially among smaller, local breeds. The rule on non-familiarity must be applied by every judge towards potential exhibitors under him.

Show day

Equipment for the day varies. Some show societies supply judging sheets, but this is unlikely at a small show, and if there is any doubt the judge should take his own, with pen and notebook.

To dress the part is vital. A great deal of skill and time has been spent on the stock on display, and neither judges nor handlers must let the animals down as far as appearances are concerned. Men should dress according to the custom for that class, usually in a suit and bowler hat. Protective clothing is occasionally necessary for some classes of stock, and apparel also depends on whether the exhibition is held indoors or outdoors, the weather and time of year.

Floral decoration of heavy-horse harness is brought to its peak in Scotland where flowers and coloured wools are lavishly used. Every detail of this cart saddle is cleaned and polished

The Suffolk breed of heavy horses has its own distinctive style of braiding manes and tails. Here is R J Clark's stallion Rowhedge Count II after his championship win at Woodbridge Show *(Audrey Wickham)*

Plaiting a tail: raffia is used to add colour; the full-length tail looks far better than the shaven variety

The shaven tail fashionable among Shire exhibitors. The judge is Mr Max Jones at the Horse of the Year Show, Wembley *(Audrey Wickham)*

Six volunteers are worth a hundred pressed men when a Shropshire ram has to be restrained at the Royal

Appropriate footwear must be worn, according to whether judging takes place on grass, tarmac, concrete or sawdust. For out of doors, warm and waterproof clothing is the rule. No one can do a good job if very cold or with wet, clammy fingers. In riding classes, judges appear in jodhpurs so as to be able to take a turn in the saddle. 'To dress the part' helps to start the day with the necessary confidence.

Car-stickers and entry passes are sent by the show society when confirming the judging appointment. Armed with these, the judge should arrive in plenty of time. Someone should be delegated to receive him, offer refreshments and introduce the stewards. From this point the judge must avoid all contact with exhibitors in his classes and, if he has time to kill, spend it in the judges' area rather than wandering about the showground.

Stewards

Stewards are important people. They are there to make the judges' onerous task as light as possible. Ring stewards should check that the right people are in the right class, and that they have their numbers. It is *not* a ring steward's responsibility to see that the exhibitors are in the assembly ring on time. That is done by loudspeaker or other stewards: 'Suffolks in the collecting ring in ten minutes.'

The judge on arrival will check or ask his stewards to check that the prize board displaying class results is in order. Organisation of the judging is left to the judge of that particular ring. It is his kingdom and there he reigns supreme.

In the ring

Though stock may be brought into the ring in any way the judge dictates, the tidiest way is in numerical order. Usually the judge asks for all to move together. Again, it is *usual* for stock to circle the ring in clockwise direction, but this may depend on the position of gates relative to the stand if there is one, and local custom.

After the entries have been about twice round, the steward is asked to stop them. That preliminary circling is simply to give a general idea of the quality of the class, to note any animals that appear really outstanding or to decide that here is a level, even class that will need sorting out in detail. The class is halted, still in a circle, but tidily, and with every animal being shown to advantage.

Examination

Then more thorough examination begins. In the case of horses, each in turn is brought out in front of the rest and checked over. The exact place is pointed to by the judge (gestures rather than words are frequently a judge's means of communication), and the groom is expected to know what is required. Then he takes his charge back to his last position. In the case of horses or bulls, the judge may ask, 'Is he all right?' before handling the animal. This is a safeguard against a kick, and the expected reply is simply 'Yes sir'. If a qualified answer is given, that animal should probably not be on the showground.

Having completed a minute check on teeth, skin, udder, neck, fetlocks and pasterns as the case may be, the judge may walk down the line refreshing his memory and checking his notes. This is still a vitally important time for exhibitors; stock *must* be looking their best.

Judging is a form of concentration, and judges have frequently been surprised at the attitudes they have struck when looking at photographs of themselves later. One certain way towards confusion is to look at stock too long, and to start changing about a lot after the provisional order has been made. It is quite possible to become literally mesmerised as a continuing circle of black and white bodies passes for minute after minute! If this happens, the judge must immediately ask the stewards to stop the line.

The centre of the ring is a very lonely place. The stewards are there to help, not to be leaned on and asked for decisions which the judge ought to give. Ringside critics congregate in groups of five or six, often placing the animals with unerring accuracy! Yet not one is in as good a position as the judge to see what is going on, and several judges have told of their thoughts that a certain entry was the tops, only to find some defect on closer inspection that was not apparent from a distance.

Cutting down numbers

In a very big class, ten or half a dozen are now called into the centre, or forward of the rest. These are the judge's pick, from which final placings will be made. The others somewhat dolefully leave the ring at this stage, in a process universally known as 'chucking out the rubbish'. This 'rubbish' may in fact contain some of the best animals in the land, but on the day they are not up to form. And the judge must judge 'on the day'.

If the leaders are not asked to step forward or into the centre, the steward is given a series of numbers of stock no longer wanted. Either method is a bit brutal, but that's showing.

Now the man in charge is left with his six or ten best. He needs a few more than there are placings for; possibly only three prizes are at stake, but there may be eight and a special. He checks over the same points again if undecided, may move the animals once more, or simply give them the keenest of eyes. The first choice is then signalled forward on the judge's left hand, followed by number two, on the right from the judge's viewpoint. This is one of the many occasions when an exhibitor must keep one eye on the animal and the other on the judge.

All is not yet won, or lost. After standing back and looking at them in order, the judge may still change his placings. If he is not happy, he may take some time over this final stage. If he is, he says to the steward: 'Yes, that's it,' and everybody claps.

Rosettes

The ring steward must have his rosettes handy at this stage. He hands them in order to the judge, according to their inscription and the colour list at that particular show. First prize in horse classes was often blue, but today is generally red. At the Royal and Royal Highland Shows, the championship rosette is red, white and blue, and the reserve champion blue and white. Red, blue, orange, and green are the colours of the first four rosettes, fifth place at the Royal being bronze, white at the Highland. Pink is the colour for sixth at the Royal, whereas the Scottish event uses bronze.

In horse classes, rosettes are placed on the bridle. In others, they are handed to exhibitors to stuff in their pockets till they reach their stalls. I have seen these precious rosettes, so hardly won, drop out of pockets before the exhibitors have left the ring!

It remains for the judge to mark his judging sheet, possibly handing a copy to a runner. School boys and girls who do this job perform an excellent service, and at shows like the Great Yorkshire where the runner service is really well organised, results are with the loudspeaker and in the Press room in a matter of minutes. They are also put up by the ring steward on the board in the judging ring.

After the prizes have been given out, and not before, competitors may ask the judge to explain his placings regarding their particular animal. During the judging, competitors must answer questions but must not ask any, or make comments. Some show societies now publish regulations to the effect that anyone engaging in conversation with the judge will be disqualified.

Special classes

At the end of the main classes come the specials. All unbeaten males may be called in, then unbeaten females. The same judge who gave them their class placings is now called to pick out the best, and is perfectly entitled to move them or go over them again. He stands back while the winners parade for him again, then points to best and reserve.

Sometimes 'challenging for the champion' involves best in breed, male or female. Here a referee judge is often needed. A person who has been judging mares and fillies or cows and heifers all morning does not readily attune his eye to stallions or bulls. He tends to think that those he spent so much time over are best; they have almost become old friends, and though they have been fairly and squarely dealt with and the 'rubbish' thrown out, he is not going to have his top animal down-placed by some upstart in a neighbouring ring. Hence the referee.

Inter-breed competitions are not easy to judge. The experienced judge looks for the best specimen of its breed, and decides how it compares with other breeds. Yet it may be preferable to judging a lot of very rough cattle, none of which is anywhere near standard. In all types, the balance of good points is what counts in the end. This balance may be most obvious when the animal walks into the ring, and that initial impression counts for a great deal—it is often the correct one.

Prices

No judge should be criticised if his top placing does not make top price in the sale that may follow. He is judging the best animal on the day, not the best line of breeding. In a small breed especially, certain blood lines have permeated so thoroughly that buyers are all trying to find a change of blood, so they leave aside the winner as being too closely related to what they already have. A judge may know full well that the Guernsey he placed third is a better milker than the first prize-winner, but she had lost her bloom and was half-way through her lactation. On the show day she was not as good.

Cattle judging

One of the toughest jobs in cattle judging concerns the production/inspection classes. Here it does not suffice to give the first three. Every animal must be placed and given its quota of points, and there may be thirty or forty of them. Some cows have to be given the lowest marks of all, whereas with other classes the lower half may be discarded all at the same time.

Size is an aspect of cattle judging that causes concern. It is easier to breed a good little animal than a good big one. Therefore the tendency exists to promote the small, neat one with correct breed points at the expense of the larger, rangier beast with scope to grow. Most breeders have fallen into this trap at some time, and most are fully aware of its dangers today. Continental imports undoubtedly shook native British breeds out of complacency, when the scale of those beasts not long removed from the yoke was appreciated.

Men who have taken part in Continental systems of panel judging have lukewarm praise for it. Lack of unanimity is a real problem; no two judges go for exactly the same type of beast.

The ideal approach

A judge's approach to the job depends inevitably on his or her personality, but there are certain standards. When officiating with young and novice exhibitors, try and put them at their ease. A light-hearted remark about some trifling misdemeanour yields far more encouragement and better results than a face of funereal gloom. Judges should never be overbearing in manner, and seldom are in the farming world.

The best judges are courteous and polite. They treat everybody alike. In the ring they appear the same to both strangers and old friends. This is not easy as a top livestock man knows many of the other men in his breed through routine business, and perhaps more than one generation of family friendship. This must have no part in decisions, nor appear to do so. It gives a bad impression if a judge laughs and jokes with one competitor, even though they are known to be old friends.

Stock must be judged on the day, and not through previous knowledge of them. Each must be treated as a complete stranger, even if the Ayrshire bull under the judge's eye was bred by him from his favourite cow. To down-grade an animal that has hitherto won everything before it calls for a certain amount of courage, but that decision is one which must be faced before allowing one's name to go on the panel of judges.

One other characteristic helps make up the ideal judge: he should keep to the time limit. There are only a limited number of minutes in the show day, and it is most unfair to those who have to use the ring later if they have to cut their activities through needlessly long spells earlier in the day. Also, the general public becomes bored with a long-drawn out affair, and their support is very necessary for next year's show.

13 Smithfield

If the great outdoor shows epitomise the best of Britain in summer, Smithfield reigns supreme as a winter event. To pass up the steps at Earls Court, London, is to enter a new world, a world of crowd and bustle, of sparkling new machinery, warm air, supremely brought-out cattle and row upon row of pigs and sheep.

To the farmer and farm worker, Smithfield's chief allurement is its contrast. The countryside in early December is dark and cold, its fields sodden, its men and women ready for a break after three months of non-stop toil as corn harvest is followed by the far more arduous business of lifting sugar-beet, potatoes and fodder roots, and sowing the maximum acreage of winter wheat before bad weather really sets in. Royal Smithfield beckons like a beacon, and farming families in their thousands respond each year.

For some, it is their annual holiday. And what better way of spending it for the ladies than a few days among London shops, coupled with a show (non-farmstock) each evening? For farmers Smithfield week is now the accepted date for so many meetings, from the Nuffield Scholars Association to Marketing Boards, that time at the show itself has to be rationed.

Such is its popularity that Smithfield is in danger of becoming bogged down through weight of numbers. Extensions in progress help stave off the evil hour, for it would be unthinkable to hold the nation's premier fatstock show outside London.

For first-time visitors, the best way to savour Smithfield's splendour is to take the lift from the entrance hall to the sheep floor, then walk directly away from the lift to the balcony. The view from there is among the best in the farming world. Row after row of machinery, each gangway filled with milling spectators, enclose the Main Ring in one corner near the cattle lines, just visible in their own annexe. On either hand are more trade stands, showing every type of mixing and milling machine, latest ideas in stock handling and identification, and feed firms each setting out to entice the passing customer.

Pens of prime fat lambs may be studied at leisure. 'I've met more people I know here than I do in six months at home,' said one Northumbrian breeder of Hill Cheviots, whose white-faced, prick-eared sheep formed one of the pens competing for the Supreme Championship.

Leisure is the keynote of Smithfield's stock lines. There is leisure to examine any desired animal in detail, leisure to stop and chat with the herdsman or shepherd, leisure to drink at one of the cheery bars with an old acquaintance not seen since last summer or the one before that. We are not going home today, so now is the chance to look, talk, and absorb knowledge. The atmosphere is pleasant, there's no threat of a sudden squall, no dust from a hot sun, no great distances to walk, and no uncommitted crowd barring the way. Almost everyone present is a fellow professional, for 97 per cent of visitors are directly concerned with agriculture. This was one of the findings of a 1976 Royal Smithfield Show survey: farmers, managers and workers constituted 64 per cent, manufacturers and suppliers associated with farming 23 per cent, while 10 per cent were lecturers and full-time students.

In 1977 the paid attendance topped 70,000, with around 10,000 overseas trade visitors admitted free. That last figure rises year by year, an indication of the value of Britain's agricultural engineering industry, and of showing's effectiveness in promoting it. Three-quarters of those present had the power to buy, specify or recommend products. Visitors spent an average of 7.6 hours at the show, and about half came specifically to see new machinery and developments.

One sad reminder is highlighted in the post-war attendance figures. In 1967 widespread foot-and-mouth disease caused livestock classes to be cancelled. Attendance that year dropped to below 21,000, compared with over 60,000 when the animals returned the next year. We stock people tend to complain about the preponderance of machinery at Smithfield, but certainly the show without stock is like a year with no spring.

'From spanners to spud harvesters, the Royal Smithfield Show offers the world's most comprehensive display of farm equipment—under one roof,' claim the organisers. 'In 1977 200 new products were introduced, and among the more unusual were a revolutionary tractor, a pea harvester to pick and shell 77 tons in a working day (enough for about $1\frac{1}{4}$ million meals), and electronic equipment for the selection of potatoes.'

Prize money totalled £15,000, competed for by nearly 1,700 animals. The 1977 sheep entry of 304 was the biggest in the show's history. Young Farmers competed in the National Stock Judging Competitions, organised by the National Federation of Young Farmers' Clubs, and for the Stockman of the Year title.

A highlight of Royal Smithfield is the Shepherd of the Year presentation. This RUMENCO/Livestock Farming award is open to men and women who do one of Britain's toughest jobs—shepherding a large flock with little assistance. Open to both hill and lowland shepherds, the award has received widespread publicity and ensured greater awareness of the dedication of shepherds and shepherdesses. Smithfield's organisers are enthusiastic about the benefits that the award has brought to the show. Every winner has stamped his or her special standards on the sheep industry, helping to ensure a bigger flow of new entrants into the profession.

No show can afford to stand still and the Earls Court event has innovations each year. The first-ever woman judge was Mrs Muriel Johnston of Courthill, Crocketford, Dumfriesshire, Scotland, who in 1977 judged the carcass cattle live in the Main Ring. Her placings were very near to the results after the cattle were slaughtered, which caused no surprise as Mrs Johnston is a very experienced exhibitor who has made show-ring decisions in many other places. She is particularly well known in the Galloway world, where one of her own animals competed in another class.

The present cost of staging the show is between £350,000 and £400,000. The British agricultural engineering industry's export figures are over £750 million a year, an incredible contrast with the early Smithfields, which were solely fatstock exhibitions. As Robert Trow-Smith tells us, the first winners in 1799 were Mr Grace's Hereford bullock, 7ft (2m) tall and weighing 1¾ tons; and Mr Poulton's 'true old Gloucester sheep', 6ft 5½in (1.96m) in girth and broader across the back, at 27in (68.5cm), than it stood high.

The site of that first Smithfield Cattle and Sheep Society competition was at Wotton's Livery Stables in Dolphin Yard, close to Smithfield Market. The show grew steadily. The original nucleus of fifty members, drawn from the nobility and gentry, renamed themselves the Smithfield Club in 1802; and in 1805 they threw open membership to all and sundry, and moved their show to Mr Sadler's yard in Goswell Street, where it remained for thirty years. The noble predominance remained for many decades, however; at the 1846 dinner, two dukes or earls spoke for every commoner tenant-farmer.

At that dinner over 130 years ago the talking points were the need to move the show from its existing site, still not far from Smithfield Market; the maintenance of good relations between stock feeder and butcher—'live and let live' remarked the noble chairman, the Duke of Richmond; and the comparative merits of Devon and Hereford beasts, which long had a 'severe contest for priority of excellence'.

Today there is still talk of moving Smithfield Show, to Birmingham of all places. Competition between Devon and Hereford is now less intense than between Continental and British breeds, but butcher and feeder are on no better terms than they ever have been or are likely to be.

There were some weird and wonderful machines in those early days, just as astonishing as today's complex electronics are to us. At the 1846 show few stands drew as many people as that of the Widow Wedlake, which had a new gorse-cutter as its centre-piece. 'From it, the furze comes out as green as new grass, and very sweet; and cows fed on it will give milk worth 30 per cent more than if they are fed on any other food.' It was worked by two men, as was Barrett's now equally extinct hand threshing machine.

Until 1839 the show continued to be held in the neighbourhood of the great Smithfield Market, from which it

originated. For the first century of its existence, the arrange-
ment was that the owners of the site took all the admis-
sion money, provided fodder for the stock and paid the
club a fee. For the first show this was £40; between the wars it
rose to over £2,000.

Soon after Queen Victoria came to the throne, no stable
yard near the market could accommodate the show. In 1839 a
move was made to one of the great sale yards, the Horse
Bazaar in that road of Sherlock Holmes fame, Baker Street.
Here the stock could be shown to better advantage, between
wide thoroughfares, under the new artificial lighting, and in
comfort. It was fit for the 'number of ladies of rank' among its
25,000 visitors.

In 1840 royalty paid its first visit to the Smithfield Show. In
1977 Her Majesty Queen Elizabeth the Queen Mother visited
the Show, following the visits of Her Majesty Queen Elizabeth
and Prince Philip in 1975, and Princess Anne in 1976.

In 1860 the Smithfield Club made a momentous move.
Larger premises had been sought for some time and Crystal
Palace, recently built for the Great Exhibition, was the first
choice. Eventually the new Agricultural Hall, on the site of
Dixon's cattle lairages, was chosen. And there at Islington the
show settled down in 1862; and there it remained until after
World War II. Its opening attracted seven royalty and 132,000
others; it was the social event of the year.

Except during the late Victorian slump years, the seventy
shows at Islington had attendances exceeding 100,000. They
also became the mirror of the growing science of farm
mechanisation. This move started in the smallest possible way
when the makers of chaff-cutters and root-slicers, used in the
feeding of show stock, were permitted to put their tackle on
view. So eager to exhibit did the hundreds of manufacturers
become that an extension to the Islington hall had to be built in
1883 to house 'the most perfect exhibition of agricultural
appliances (and animal medicines) to be found in the kingdom'.

During the next half century the farm machinery developed
faster than the livestock. Binders, mowers and ploughs from
Ransomes and others improved steadily, while milking

machines and tractors arrived in the decade before World War I.

Things changed more slowly in the livestock world. Early cattle championships went to the Durham Oxen, prototypes of the beef Shorthorn, to Herefords or Devons. From the 1840s to 1866, Herefords, Devons and Shorthorns shared the gold medals for the champion beasts. In 1866 a 'Shorthorn-Scotch polled ox' came to the top. After 1867, when the great William McCombie's rising five-year-old Aberdeen Angus ox won the male championship cup, Scottish breeds began to dominate the show. They did so until the 1960s and the establishment of Continental breeds in Britain.

Only once before 1919 did a beast under two years old and not grossly over-fat win the cup. For the first century of the show's history, its prize-winners were monstrous animals, whose carcasses were covered with mountains of fat. To some extent they met the needs of the times: for tallow candles, and for the huge sides that were salted for use at sea. Today's visitor sees stock fashioned for modern needs, and giving a lead to the meat producing industry. The Smithfield we know today becomes even more enthralling when a little is known of its past fortunes and changes.

A sample contemporary programme reads: 'Second Day, Tuesday, 9 am Show opens. Visit of HRH the Duke of Gloucester, GCVO' with the following timetable:

9.15 am Judging of Pigs (Porker classes) in Pig Ring

9.30 am Judging of Cattle Overall Championships in Main Ring

11.00 am 'Export Lamb' Sheep Demonstration in Sheep Ring

11.30 am Parade of Sheep in Sheep Ring, with commentary by Mr A. Veitch, OBE

12.45 pm Presentation of RUMENCO/Livestock Farming Shepherd of the Year Award in Main Ring

1.45 pm 'Options for Beef' Demonstration in Main Ring

2.00 pm Judging of Pig Overall Championships in Pig Ring

2.30 pm Judging of Cattle Breed Championships in Main Ring

2.30 pm Auction Sale of Live Sheep in Sheep Ring
(Champion and Reserve Champion at 3.00 pm)
4.30 pm YFC Stockman of the Year Competition in Main
Ring
6.00 pm Show closes

A series of practical demonstrations takes place throughout
the show. These vary from year to year, the 1977 sample
including 'Options for Beef', a study of the Agricultural
Development and Advisory Services suckler herds. Eight
breeds are used in different combinations in the four herds. At
Pwllpeiran, high and wet in the Welsh hills near Aberystwyth,
the local Welsh Black breed is kept, and two pure-bred steers
were exhibited. From Redesdale in Northumberland, a drier
but colder farm, Blue Grey cows are crossed with Charolais to
give growth rates that the lowland fattener can exploit.
Liscombe on the Somerset/Devon border has introduced extra
milk by top-crossing Devon/Friesian cows with their other
local breed, the South Devon, growthy enough to challenge the
Charolais for size. Hereford/Friesian females crossed with a
Lincoln Red are the choice at High Mowthorpe in the
Yorkshire Wolds. Smithfield brought a reprieve for two of their
steers, which under normal farm practice would have been killed
as bulls six months previously. Eight steers representing the
different systems were paraded in the Main Ring as part of the
combined livestock demonstration from the Meat and
Livestock Commission and the Milk Marketing Board.

The Milk Marketing Board's 'Options for Beef' showed
cattle sired by bulls of the popular beef breeds whose semen is
available through the Board. The Meat and Livestock
Commission stressed the importance of choosing the right time
to slaughter cattle, and demonstrated handling to assess
fatness.

In the Export Lamb Demonstration, selected lamb
carcasses fit for 90 per cent of European customers were
shown. The five main carcass faults were also spotlighted; too
fat; too plain; excessive kidney knob; bruised; or abscesses
caused by faulty inoculation techniques.

Entire male pigs give better conversion of feed into lean meat, according to ADAS and the Agricultural Research Council in the pigs corner at Smithfield. Four pens of live pigs illustrated the treatment being compared. The savings in feed and labour expected in a 200-sow herd were dealt with in this section, and Smithfield visitors were advised to secure their market outlet before ceasing castration. It was one more example of the show's present down-to-earth policy.

The importance of the pig industry to Smithfield was underlined by a joint Fatstock Marketing Corporation/National Pig Breeders' Association display. Live pigs in each of the four weight ranges were shown, and the commercial suitability of carcasses demonstrated by a butcher. Marketing pigs at two weight ranges only may be necessary when Britain is completely integrated in the EEC, and this possibility was discussed.

Not least in importance were the Lamb and Pork Carcass Cutting Demonstrations staged by the Smithfield College for the Distributive Trades. A side of pork was cut, displayed and labelled, pork chops were cut, and a leg of pork boned and rolled.

A butcher was also present at the Children's Sheep Demonstration, in which several almost extinct breeds were paraded, cuts of meat were described, and a sheep was shorn and the wool spun by hand. Sheepskin jackets and woollen clothes were modelled.

Perhaps the most exciting and fascinating Smithfield events are the auction sales traditionally conducted by Hobsons. The Supreme Champion beast may be reserved up to £1,000, but this figure is in fact multiplied several times before the hammer falls. Though butchers naturally like to place rosettes in their windows, the many quality non-winners find satisfactory outlets at Smithfield. The show remains primarily a fatstock show, and almost all stock entered goes to the abattoir.

This, then, is Smithfield, the week when the country comes to town. Among the assorted array of the capital's population, the farmers stand out. Rugged of neck, wearing strong tweed suits and speaking in country accents ranging from Cornwall to the Orkneys, with a strong sprinkling of unmistakable Welsh, they move uncertainly through the Underground stations, ill at ease among the crowds, unable to walk with anything like a proper stride on the pavements. A placard on each proclaiming 'I make my living tending livestock' is quite needless, for each bears his profession proudly on his face and in his gait. Long may the farming community remain a thing apart, easily distinguishable from the rest.

My favourite Smithfield-week story concerns a north-country farmer who found himself in a night club during the year of the great straw shortage, when clean straw was fetching a high price. A straw-skirted hostess perched herself on our friend's knee. Not at all taken aback, he fingered the skirt and said: 'That's a bit of right stuff, lass. I wish I had a few tons of it at home under my Dutch barn!'

Inevitably, as farming becomes more sophisticated, the strangeness of London will wear off. But those first visits to Smithfield must remain among life's highlights to those of us who experienced them when the day-to-day world was bounded by the horizons of our own farms.

14   The Future

What of the future? I hope that there will be more rather than less people working on the land, but that they will be equipped with the best that modern technology can offer, that they will be prosperous and have some leisure. If so, the agricultural show will be a bigger attraction than ever, to point the way with the latest innovations and to provide spectacles of animal grace and power.

Shows will become more international in cháracter. (Sir Barnes Wallis is working on a design for an aircraft that will reach Australia from London in two and a half hours. If this happens we may set off for the Sydney Show after an early breakfast, just as we do for the English Royal, the Royal Welsh or the Royal Highland today!) The Royal Easter Show at Sydney is but one overseas magnet. Amsterdam, Brussels and Berlin all hold agricultural shows in January/February. The Paris Show in early March attracts over 800,000 visitors a year, with entries and exhibitors from over sixty countries. Some 12,000 machines are on display; there is an international dog and poultry show, and displays of food and wine products as well as farm livestock.

At Verona, also in March, East meets West and Eastern bloc countries are targets both for British livestock exporters and machinery importers. A horse-drawn grass mower is being imported from the Balkans, home firms having given up production for the time being.

In April the Saragossa exhibition takes place in Spain, with a West German show in late April and early May held every second year in one of three venues. Over 300,000 visitors from all over the world gain information on marketing and management problems as well as watching livestock classes and sales.

The Dublin Spring Show and Industries Fair takes place in early May; Jönköping, Sweden, in early June; and the Kenyan

International Agricultural Trade Fair at Nairobi in late September. Winter shows at Toronto and Regina are Canadian attractions, while the Calgary Stampede is sufficient reason for a visit there.

Different judging systems will be tried in years to come. Shows must be seen to be leaders and not followers of agricultural fashion. Classes confined to animals that have already achieved certain standards of performance, or whose parents are superior producers, are suggested by Hereford breeder Mr Oscar Colburn. To some extent this already occurs in production/conformation classes.

All stock breeders and exhibitors can learn from each other. Foxhounds at Peterborough, Thoroughbred horses at Newmarket and Simmental cattle at Stafford may seem to inhabit different worlds from fish farmers and poultry exhibitors, yet all belong to the great profession of livestock production. In endeavouring to see that each generation betters the last, the shows have an irreplaceable part to play.

Glossary

ADAS Agricultural Development and Advisory Service

BALANCE Harmonious relationship of all body parts, blended for symmetry and pleasing appearance

BLOOM A shining, clean, lustrous coat indicating good health; impossible to achieve in an unfit animal

BREEDER Owner of the animal's dam at the time of birth

BREED CHARACTERISTICS Features that distinguish one breed from another; correct ones are a show-ring 'must'

BY Designates the sire

CASTRATE Make incapable of breeding (male)

CLEY One of the parts of a cloven hoof

COD Scrotal sac after castration, ie without testicles

CONFORMATION Form of an animal, determined by structural shape and muscling

CORONET Part of the horse's pastern, which is fetlock to hoof

CROSSBRED An animal whose parents are of different breeds. In fat cattle classes the cross may be three-way, eg Angus × Shorthorn/Galloway. The recognised agricultural practice is to name the sire first, but this rule is not always followed by breeders, or by show secretaries who rely on breeders' information.

CULL An animal taken from the herd because of its poor quality

DROPPED Born

DAM Mother

DRAFT EWE One being sold from the hills, where it was born and reared, to easier conditions lower down. Ewes are drafted at regular ages, usually five or six years old—sold for breeding half-bred lambs, they are not throw-outs.

FINISH The degree of fatness; stock being 'finished' or 'fed' are in the final stages of fattening

GIMMER Young female sheep—gimmer lamb, gimmer hogg (until its first clipping), gimmer shearling (after being clipped for the first time)

GRADING Carcass classification of the live animal

HOGG See gimmer. A wether or tup hogg is one from the end of the year in which it is born to shearing.

INBREEDING Mating of closely related animals, eg father to daughter

KILLING-OUT PERCENTAGE Proportion of saleable meat to hide and offal

LINE BREEDING Mating of animals less closely related than in inbreeding, eg daughter to grandsire or cousin to cousin

MARBLING Fat distributed throughout the lean; vital to the quality animal, different from knobs of fat over the kidneys, etc

OUT OF Designates dam

PARTURITION Act of birth

PEDIGREE Table or chart showing line of ancestry

PERFORMANCE TEST Measure of individual performance, particularly rate of growth, and carcass traits

POLLED Hornless

PROGENY TEST Evaluation of a sire through his progeny; milk yields of a bull's daughters may be compared with those of their dams

RAM, TUP Male sheep for breeding

REGISTRATION An animal's entry in herd or flock book; each is given a number, often needed on show entries.

SEED STOCK Foundation animals for establishing a herd or flock

SERVICE Mating

SHEARLING Sheep from between first and second shearings, ie between about 16 months and 2 years 4 months

STEER Castrated male or bullock (cattle)

TATTOO Identification mark, usually a number in the ear

TUP Ram

WEDGING The condition of a newly-calven cow, whose mammary tissue becomes swollen and liable to cause discomfort

WETHER Castrated male sheep

Bibliography

Beeson, Norby & Hunsley. *Livestock Judging and Evaluation* (USA, 1972)

Bowen, Godfrey. *Wool Away!* (Whitcombe & Tombs, 1955)

Chivers, Keith. *The Shire Horse: A History of the Breed, the Society and the Men* (J A Allen, 1976, Futura, 1978)

Cooper, M M & Thomas R J. *Profitable Sheep Farming* (Farming Press, 1975)

Cooper M M & Willis M B. *Profitable Beef Production* (Farming Press, 1977)

Davidson, H R. *Production & Marketing of Pigs* (Longman, 1966)

Fraser, Allan. *Sheep Farming* (Crosby Lockwood, 1937)

Fraser, Allan & Stamp, J T. *Sheep Husbandry and Diseases* (Crosby Lockwood, 1968)

Fream, *Elements of Agriculture* (ed D H. Robinson) (J Murray, 1972)

Goodwin, Derek. *Beef Management and Production* (Hutchinson, 1977)

Halnan, E T *et al*. *Principles and Practice of Feeding Farm Animals* (Longmans, Green & Co, 1966)

Hart, Edward. *Golden Guinea Book of Heavy Horse Past and Present* (David & Charles 1976)

Hart, Edward. *Northcountry Farm Animals* (Dalesman, 1976)

Hetherington, Lois. *All About Goats* (Farming Press, 1977)

Johnson, Geoffrey. *Profitable Pig Farming* (Farming Press, 1976)

Jones, Elwyn. *Just Your Meat* (National Federation of YFCs)

Keegan, Terry. *The Heavy Horse: Its Harness & Harness Decoration* (Pelham Books, 1973)

Mason, I L. *Dictionary of Livestock Breeds, Types and Varieties* (Commonwealth Agricultural Bureau, 1969)

National Sheep Association. *British Sheep* (NSA, 1976)

Russell, Kenneth. *Herdsman's Book* (ed S Williams) (Farming Press, 1974)

Russell, Kenneth. *Principles of Dairy Farming* (ed S Williams) (Farming Press, 1974)

Ryder, M L & Stephenson, S K. *Wool Growth* (Academic Press, 1968)

Salmon, Jill. *Goatkeeper's Guide* (David & Charles, 1976)

Watmough, W. *Practical Inbreeding* (Watmoughs, Idle, 1973)

Whitlock, R. *Bulls Through The Ages* (Lutterworth Press, 1977)

World Shorthorn Conference Full Report, South Africa 1974

Youtz, H G & Carlson, A C. *Judging Livestock, Dairy Cattle and Crops* (Prentice-Hall, 1970)

The Shows

(Attendance figures not available in every case)

		Attendance
HUNTERS' IMPROVEMENT AND NATIONAL LIGHT HORSE BREEDING SOCIETY Newmarket, Suffolk	*March*	
SHIRE HORSE SOCIETY Peterborough, Cambs	*March*	6,000
ALL ENGLAND JUMPING COURSE Hickstead, Sussex	*Late April/ Early May*	
ROYAL DUBLIN SOCIETY RDS Showgrounds, Ballsbridge, Dublin 4, Ireland	*May*	238,780
NEWARK AND NOTTINGHAMSHIRE AGRICULTURAL SOCIETY Showground, Winthorpe, Newark, Notts	*May*	62,940
ROYAL WINDSOR HORSE SHOW CLUB Home Park, Windsor, Berks	*May*	
SOUTH SUFFOLK AGRICULTURAL SOCIETY Bridge Street Farm, Long Melford, Sudbury, Suffolk	*May*	6,500
SHROPSHIRE AND WEST MIDLANDS AGRICULTURAL SOCIETY Shrewsbury, Salop	*May*	55,330
TYNESIDE COUNTRY FAIR Stannington, Northumberland	*May*	
DEVON COUNTY AGRICULTURAL ASSOCIATION Exeter, Devon	*May*	106,600
HUMBERSIDE COUNTY SHOW Beverley Racecourse, North Humberside	*May*	34,200
BRITISH PERCHERON HORSE SOCIETY Mill Lodge Equestrian Centre, Outwell, Wisbech, Cambs	*May*	3,000
STAFFORDSHIRE AGRICULTURAL SOCIETY County Showground, Stafford	*May*	42,000
ROYAL ULSTER AGRICULTURAL SOCIETY Balmoral, Belfast	*May*	
HEATHFIELD AND DISTRICT AGRICULTURAL SHOW SOCIETY Little Tottingworth Farm, Broad Oak, Heathfield, Sussex	*May*	16,000
HERTFORDSHIRE AGRICULTURAL SOCIETY Friar's Wash, Redbourn, Nr St Albans, Herts	*May*	39,000
WHARFEDALE AGRICULTURAL SOCIETY Bridge End, Otley, West Yorks	*May*	25,000
WARRINGTON HORSE SOCIETY Walton Park, Warrington, Cheshire	*May*	6,370

DERBYSHIRE AGRICULTURAL AND HORTICULTURAL
SOCIETY
Elvaston Castle Country Park, Derby   *May*   16,000

NORTH SOMERSET AGRICULTURAL SOCIETY
Ashton Court, Bristol   *May*   16,500

SURREY COUNTY AGRICULTURAL SOCIETY
Stoke Park, Guildford, Surrey   *May*   50,000

WOODHALL SPA AND DISTRICT AGRICULTURAL SOCIETY
Jubilee Park, Woodhall Spa, Lincs   *May*   10,000

WETHERBY AGRICULTURAL SOCIETY
The Grange Park, Wetherby, West Yorks   *May*   12,000

SUFFOLK AGRICULTURAL ASSOCIATION   *Late May/*
The Showground, Ipswich, Suffolk   *Early June*   45,680

ROYAL BATH AND WEST AND SOUTHERN COUNTIES
SOCIETY   *Late May/*
The Showground, Shepton Mallet, Somerset   *Early June*   121,190

ALL ENGLAND JUMPING COURSE
Hickstead, Sussex   *June*

DEEPING ST JAMES AND DISTRICT AGRICULTURAL SOCIETY
Stamford Road, Market Deeping, Lincs   *June*   12,000

HACKNEY HORSE SOCIETY
Ardingly, Sussex   *June*

ROYAL CORNWALL AGRICULTURAL ASSOCIATION
Wadebridge, Cornwall   *June*   86,000

SOUTH OF ENGLAND AGRICULTURAL SOCIETY
Ardingly, Haywards Heath, Sussex   *June*   89,750

LEICESTERSHIRE AGRICULTURAL SOCIETY
Derby Road, Loughborough, Leics   *June*   9,000

THREE COUNTIES AGRICULTURAL SOCIETY
Malvern, Worcs   *June*   47,300

ESSEX AGRICULTURAL SOCIETY
The Showground, Great Leighs, Chelmsford, Essex   *June*   66,000

BISHOPS WALTHAM AND DISTRICT AGRICULTURAL
SOCIETY
Droxford, Hants   *June*   7,500

ROYAL HIGHLAND AND AGRICULTURAL SOCIETY OF
SCOTLAND
Ingliston, Newbridge, Lothian   *June*   127,300

LINCOLNSHIRE AGRICULTURAL SOCIETY
Lincoln   *June*   69,300

BRITISH DRIVING SOCIETY
Smith's Lawn, Windsor, Berks   *June*

HUNTERS' IMPROVEMENT AND NATIONAL LIGHT HORSE
BREEDING SOCIETY
Shrewsbury, Salop   *June*

ROYAL NORFOLK AGRICULTURAL ASSOCIATION
Showground, Dereham Road, New Costessy, Norwich,
Norfolk   *June*   94,590

ROYAL AGRICULTURAL SOCIETY OF ENGLAND National Agricultural Centre, Stoneleigh, Kenilworth, Warwicks	*July*	196,840
SOUTHAMPTON SHOW The Common, Southampton, Hants	*July*	58,100
TENDRING HUNDRED FARMERS' CLUB Lawford House Park, Manningtree, Essex	*July*	12,400
BRIDGEND SHOW SOCIETY Bridgend, Mid-Glamorgan	*July*	6,000
YORKSHIRE AGRICULTURAL SOCIETY Harrogate, North York	*July*	124,400
KENT COUNTY AGRICULTURAL SOCIETY Detling, Nr Maidstone, Kent	*July*	62,500
GREAT ECCLESTON AGRICULTURAL SOCIETY Great Eccleston, Preston, Lancs	*July*	9,000
HEREFORD CITY COUNCIL CARNIVAL	*July*	130,000
FULMER IN HAND SHOW Alderbourne Lane, Fulmer, Bucks	*July*	
ROYAL INTERNATIONAL HORSE SHOW Empire Pool, Wembley, Middx	*July*	50,000
EAST OF ENGLAND AGRICULTURAL SOCIETY East of England Showground, Peterborough, Cambs	*July*	154,700
PETERBOROUGH ROYAL FOXHOUND SHOW SOCIETY East of England Showground, Peterborough, Cambs	*July*	
CUMBERLAND AGRICULTURAL SOCIETY Bitts Park, Carlisle, Cumbria	*July*	24,500
MALTON AGRICULTURAL SOCIETY Malton, North Yorks	*July*	11,440
ROYAL ISLE OF WIGHT AGRICULTURAL SOCIETY The Showground, Northwood, Isle of Wight	*July*	27,300
THE LIVERPOOL SHOW Wavertree, Liverpool	*July*	one day
ASHBY AND DISTRICT AGRICULTURAL SOCIETY Calke Park, Ticknall, Derbys	*July*	10,000
ROYAL WELSH AGRICULTURAL SOCIETY Llanelwedd, Builth Wells, Powys	*July*	111,000
NANTWICH AND SOUTH CHESHIRE SHOW Dorfold Hall Park, Nantwich, Cheshire	*July*	21,000
NEW FOREST AGRICULTURAL SHOW SOCIETY New Park, Brockenhurst, Hants	*July*	38,000
ARAB HORSE SOCIETY Ascot, Berks	*July*	3,000
COUNTRY LANDOWNERS' ASSOCIATION GAME FAIR Kinmount, Annan, Dumfries	*July*	92,000
METROPOLITAN POLICE HORSE SHOW AND TOURNAMENT Mounted Branch Training Establishment, Imber Court, East Moseley, Surrey	*July*	11,000
NORTHAMPTON BOROUGH COUNCIL SHOW Abington Park, Northampton	*July*	40,000

ABERGAVENNY AND BORDER COUNTIES SHOW Glebe Lands, Llanwenarth, Abergavenny, Gwent	*July*	17,000
LEEK AND DISTRICT SOCIETY Birchall, Leek, Staffs	*July*	15,000
THE NATIONAL PONY SHOW Three Counties Showground, Malvern, Worcs	*August*	
BAKEWELL AGRICULTURAL AND HORTICULTURAL SOCIETY Bakewell, Derbys	*August*	40,000
HONITON AND DISTRICT AGRICULTURAL ASSOCIATION Honiton, Devon	*August*	19,500
OSWESTRY AND DISTRICT AGRICULTURAL SOCIETY Parkhall Camp, Whittington Road, Oswestry, Salop	*August*	12,500
ALL ENGLAND JUMPING COURSE Hickstead, Sussex	*August*	
THE SOUTHSEA SHOW Southsea, Hants	*August*	52,000
RUTLAND AGRICULTURAL SOCIETY Oakham, Rutland	*August*	9,000
ROYAL DUBLIN SOCIETY RDS Showgrounds, Ballsbridge, Dublin 4	*August*	150,900
AIREDALE AGRICULTURAL SOCIETY Myrtle Park, Bingley, West Yorks	*August*	21,000
NORTH WALES AGRICULTURAL SOCIETY Tyddyn Hen, Caernarfon, Gwynedd	*August*	
SHROPSHIRE HORTICULTURAL SOCIETY The Quarry, Shrewsbury, Salop	*August*	80,000
GREAT NORTHUMBERLAND SHOW Stannington, Northumberland	*August*	
MAPLEDURWELL SHOW Rushmoor Arena, Aldershot, Hants	*August*	
FILLONGLEY AGRICULTURAL SOCIETY Corley, Coventry	*August*	5,000
SOUTHWELL SHOW Norwood Park, Southwell, Notts	*August*	9,500
ANGLESEY AGRICULTURAL SOCIETY Mona, Llangefni, Gwynedd	*August*	47,500
VALE OF GLAMORGAN AGRICULTURAL SOCIETY Penllyn Castle Park, Cowbridge, South Glamorgan	*August*	10,000
PEMBROKESHIRE AGRICULTURAL SOCIETY Withybush, Haverfordwest, Dyfed	*August*	35,000
DENBIGHSHIRE AND FLINTSHIRE AGRICULTURAL SOCIETY Bryn Cwnin and Cwybr Farms, Rhyl, Clwyd	*August*	22,000
ASHBOURNE SHIRE HORSE SOCIETY Polo Ground, Osmaston, Ashbourne, Derbys	*August*	
MID-SOMERSET AGRICULTURAL SOCIETY Shepton Mallet, Somerset	*August*	
GILLINGHAM AND SHAFTESBURY AGRICULTURAL SOCIETY Gillingham, Dorset	*August*	12,000

BRITISH TIMKEN SHOW Duston, Northants	*August*	40,000
EGHAM AND THORPE ROYAL AGRICULTURAL AND HORTICULTURAL ASSOCIATION Milton Park Farm, Egham, Surrey	*August*	9,000
HARLOW SHOW Town Park, Harlow, Essex	*August*	42,500
ALL ENGLAND JUMPING COURSE Hickstead, Sussex	*August*	
COUNTRY SPORTS AT THE TOWN AND COUNTRY FESTIVAL British Field Sports Society in conjunction with The National Agricultural Centre, Stoneleigh, Warwicks	*August*	
EXPO STEAM TRANSPORT AND COUNTRY FAIR East of England Showground, Peterborough, Cambs	*August*	70,000
AYLSHAM SHOW Blickling Park, Aylsham, Norwich, Norfolk	*August*	20,000
EDENBRIDGE AND OXTED AGRICULTURAL SHOW Edenbridge, Kent	*August*	23,000
KENILWORTH AND DISTRICT AGRICULTURAL SOCIETY The Royal Showground, Kenilworth, Warwicks	*August*	71,500
MADRESFIELD AGRICULTURAL SOCIETY Madresfield Court, Malvern, Hereford and Worcs	*August*	11,000
MOORGREEN SHOW—GREASLEY, SELSTON AND EASTWOOD AGRICULTURAL SOCIETY Front Park, Watnall, Notts	*August*	33,000
NORTH-EAST HANTS AGRICULTURAL ASSOCIATION 'ALTON SHOW' Anstey Park, Alton, Hants	*August*	15,500
CITY OF LEICESTER HORSE SHOW The Oval, Abbey Park, Leics	*August*	60,000
MELPLASH AGRICULTURAL SOCIETY Bridport, Dorset	*August*	11,000
MONMOUTHSHIRE AGRICULTURAL SHOW SOCIETY Vauxhall, Monmouth	*August*	20,000
THE DONKEY BREED SOCIETY AND BRITISH SUPREME CHAMPIONSHIP SHOW National Equestrian Centre, Stoneleigh, Kenilworth, Warwicks	*September*	
DORCHESTER AGRICULTURAL SOCIETY Came Park, Dorchester, Dorset	*September*	15,000
HENLEY AND DISTRICT AGRICULTURAL ASSOCIATION Marlow Road Field, Henley-on-Thames, Oxon	*September*	4,000
MORETON-IN-MARSH AND DISTRICT AGRICULTURAL AND HORSE SHOW SOCIETY Moreton-in-Marsh, Glos	*September*	15,000
ORSETT HORTICULTURAL AND AGRICULTURAL SOCIETY Orsett Hall, Orsett, Essex	*September*	
WOLSINGHAM AND WEAR AGRICULTURAL SOCIETY Wolsingham, Co Durham	*September*	6,500

BRITISH SHOW PONY SOCIETY East of England Showground, Alwalton, Peterborough, Cambs	*September*	1,500
BUCKS COUNTY AGRICULTURAL ASSOCIATION Hartwell Park, Aylesbury, Bucks	*September*	18,000
ROMSEY AGRICULTURAL AND HORSE SHOW SOCIETY Broadlands Park, Romsey, Hants	*September*	22,800
COLLINGHAM FARMERS' CLUB The Showground, Winthorpe, Newark, Notts	*September*	
NEWBURY AND DISTRICT AGRICULTURAL SOCIETY Siege Cross, Thatcham, Newbury, Berks	*September*	34,000
BRITISH CHAROLAIS CATTLE SOCIETY—WORLD CHAROLAIS CONVENTION Harrogate, North Yorks	*September*	
ROYAL ASSOCIATION OF BRITISH DAIRY FARMERS National Agricultural Centre, Stoneleigh, Kenilworth, Warwicks	*September*	12,900
THAME AGRICULTURAL ASSOCIATION Thame Show, Oxon	*September*	25,000
WOKINGHAM AND DISTRICT AGRICULTURAL ASSOCIATION White House Farm, Spencer Wood, Reading, Berks	*September*	
HORSE OF THE YEAR SHOW Empire Pool, Wembley	*October*	50,000
NORTH WESTERN DAIRY SHOW Bingley Hall, Stafford	*October*	
THE SOCIETY OF PLOUGHMEN LTD Blagdon, Newcastle, Northumberland	*October*	
ROYAL SMITHFIELD SHOW Earls Court, London SW5	*December*	

Index